INSTRUCTOR'S RESOURCE GUIDE

to accompany

A Problem Solving Approach to Mathematics

for Elementary School Teachers

Seventh Edition

Rick Billstein

Shlomo Libeskind

Johnny W. Lott

Addison
Wesley

Boston San Francisco New York
London Toronto Sydney Tokyo Singapore Madrid
Mexico City Munich Paris Cape Town Hong Kong Montreal

Reproduced by Addison Wesley Longman Publishing Company Inc. from camera-ready copy supplied by the authors.

ISBN   0-201-61143-0

1 2 3 4 5 6 7 8 9 10 VG 03 02 01 00

TABLE OF CONTENTS

TABLE OF CONTENTS

The authors want to thank Barbara McCann for her work in typing this manuscript.
R B., S L., and J.W.L.

Sample Assessment

1. List the terms that complete a possible pattern in each of the following:

   (a)   38, 33, 28, 23, 18, ___,___,___
   (b)   640, 320, 160, 80, ___,___,___
   (c)   7, 8, 15, 23, 38, ___,___,___
   (d)   4, 8, 16, 32, 64, ___,___,___
   (e)   1, ___,___,___, 25, 36, 49

2. Classify each of the sequences in Problem 1 as arithmetic, geometric, or neither. Tell why in each case.
   (a)

   (b)

   (c)

   (d)

   (e)

3. Find the nth term in each of the following:

   (a)   6, 8, 10, 12, 14, ...

   (b)   2, 5, 10, 17, 26, ...

   (c)   5, 25, 125, 625, ...

4. Find the first five terms of the sequences with the nth term given as follows:

   (a) $3n + 2$
         _____
         _____
         _____
         _____
         _____

(b) $n^2 + n$

_____
_____
_____
_____
_____

(c) $n(n + 7)$

_____
_____
_____
_____
_____

5. Find the following sum.

_____ $6 + 8 + 10 + 12 + ... + 100$

6. (a)   Determine a possible pattern in the following.

101, 212, 323, 434, 545, 656, 767, ...

(b)   What is the 100th term of the sequence in (a)?

7. A person writing a book numbered the pages consecutively starting with 1 and had written 4553 digits. How many pages had she numbered? Explain your reasoning.

8. Place the numbers 3, 4, 7, 9 in the squares below to obtain the greatest product.

□ □
× □ □
‾‾‾‾‾‾

9. John is responsible for seating arrangements at a dinner party. He has seven tables that individually seat six people as shown. He wants to make one large table by pushing them together. He expects a total of 15 couples.

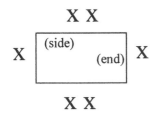

(a) Can he accommodate all the expected guests if he lines the tables up side-to-side? Explain.

(b) Can he accommodate all the expected guests if he lines the tables up end-to-end? Explain.

10. (a) Use 4 and 5 as the first two terms of a Fibonacci-type sequence. Find the first six terms.

    _____, _____, _____, _____, _____, _____

    (b) Write a description of a Fibonacci-type sequence using a recursive formula.

11. A rectangle is 6 cm wide. The length is 1 cm less than 3 times the width.

    (a) What is the length of the rectangle?_____

    (b) What is the perimeter of the rectangle?_____

12. How many different ways can you make change for a $100 bill using $5, $10, $20, and $50 bills.

13. How many different rectangles are in the following figure? _____

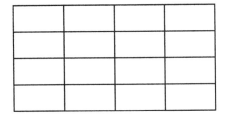

14. Solve the following for x.
    (a) $2x - 4 = 14$

    (b) $5(x + 3) = 15 - x$

15. Translate the following into an algebraic expression or an algebraic equation.
    Take any number. Multiply it by 7. Add 13. Divide the result by 2. The answer is 13.

16. Choose one problem solving strategy and write a problem that could be solved with the strategy identified.

*17. Which of the following are statements?
    _____   (a) She has blond hair.

    _____   (b) $2 + x = x + 2$

*18. Negate each of the following:
(a) All mathematics problems are easy.

(b) Some numbers are not natural numbers.

*19. Consider the following statement: If a bird is a Western Tanager, then it has a red head. Write each of the following:
(a) The converse of the statement.

(b) The contrapositive of the statement.

(c) The inverse of the statement.

*20. Find a valid conclusion for the following argument:
If a person uses a calculator, she makes fewer computation errors than one who does not.
Rose uses a calculator.

1. (a) 13, 8, 3
    (b) 40, 20, 10
    (c) 61, 99, 160
    (d) 128, 256, 512
    (e) 4, 9, 16

2. (a) The series is arithmetic. The common difference is ⁻5.
    (b) The series is geometric. The common ratio is 1/2.
    (c) The series is neither arithmetic nor geometric. It is a Fibonacci-type sequence where
         each term (after the second) is found by adding the two previous terms.
    (d) The series is geometric with common ratio 2.
    (e) The series is neither arithmetic nor geometric. It is formed by squaring.

3. (a) $2n + 4$
    (b) $n^2 + 1$
    (c) 5^n

4. (a) 5, 8, 11, 14, 17
    (b) 2, 6, 12, 20, 30
    (c) 8, 18, 30, 44, 60

5. 2544

6. (a) $(n + 1)$st term = nth term + 111
    (b) 11090

7. 1415

    There are 9 pages with a one-digit number, 90 pages with a two-digit number, 900 pages
    with a three-digit number, and so on. Since $9 \cdot 1 + 90 \cdot 2 + 900 \cdot 3 = 2889$ digits, she must
    be past page 999. (Check that she hasn't yet reached page 9999.) She is now numbering
    pages with four-digit page numbers, so the number of digits she has written is:
    $9 \cdot 1 + 90 \cdot 2 + 900 \cdot 3 + p \cdot 4$, or $2889 + 4 \cdot p$, where p is the number of pages past 999.
    Because she has written 4553 digits, $4553 = 2889 + 4p$. Consequently:

    $4553 - 2889 = 4p$
    $1664 = 4p$
    $p = 416$

    Therefore, she has numbered 416 pages past 999 and therefore a total of 1415 pages.

8. 74×93

9. (a) No. Fifteen couples are 30 people. Seven tables in a side-to-side arrangement will
         only seat 18. There can be four at each end table and 2 per table at each of the other
         five tables, for a total of 18.

(b)   Yes. The five tables in the middle of this arrangement can seat four people. The two end tables can seat five people. Consequently, John can seat 5 • 4 + 2 • 5 or 30 people with this arrangement.

10.   (a)   4, 5, 9, 14, 23, 37
(b) A recursive formula might be the following:
$(n + 1)$st term = nth term + $(n - 1)$st term

11.   (a)   17 cm
(b)   46 cm

12.   49 ways if not all must be used at any given time

13.   100 rectangles

14.   (a)   9
(b)   0

15.   Let n be any number. The expression then will be $(7n +13)/2 = 13$.

16.   The answers will vary depending on the strategy chosen.

*17.   (a)   Not a statement
(b)   Statement

*18.   (a)   There exists a mathematics problem that is not easy.
(b)   All numbers are natural numbers.

*19.   (a)   If a bird has a red head, then it is a Western Tanager.
(b)   If a bird does not have a red head, then it is not a Western Tanager.
(c)   If a bird is not a Western Tanager, then it does not have a red head.

*20.   Rose makes fewer computation errors than one who does not use a calculator.

8 CHAPTER 1 FORM B

Sample Assessment

1. List the terms that complete a possible pattern in each of the following:

   (a) 47, 87, 67, 107, 87,___,___,___
   (b) 2, 10, 50, 250, 1250,___,___,___
   (c) 8, 15, 22, 29, 36,___,___,___
   (d) 4, 0, 8, 0, 16, 0,___,___,___
   (e) 5, 9, 13, 17, 21,___,___,___

2. Classify each of the sequences in Problem 1 as arithmetic, geometric, or neither.
   (a)

   (b)

   (c)

   (d)

   (e)

3. Fine the nth term in each of the following:

   (a) 4, 9, 14, 19, 24,...

   _____

   (b) 6, 12, 24, 48, 96,...

   _____

   (c) 1, 4, 9, 16, 25,...

   _____

4. Find the first five terms of the sequences with the nth term given as follows:

   (a) $4n + 7$

   _____
   _____
   _____
   _____
   _____

   (b) $n^2 + 2n$

   _____
   _____
   _____
   _____
   _____

(c) $n(n-1)$

_____
_____
_____
_____
_____

5. Find the following sum:
   $3 + 6 + 9 + 12 + ... + 84$

6. In order to divide a P.E. class into two teams, the gym teacher has the students stand in a circle and count off 1, 2, 3, ... all the way around the circle. If the teacher divides the circle in half between the numbers 3 and 4 and between the number 12 and 13, how many students are on each team?

7. A 200–mL test tube collects 25 mL of condensation every night and loses 9 mL to evaporation every day. When will the test tube overflow? Explain your reasoning.

8. Charlie is designing an 80 ft by 120 ft rectangular fence. He wants to put posts 10 ft apart along one of the 120 ft sides. The posts will be 8 ft apart along the other three sides of the fence. How many posts does Charlie need? Explain your reasoning.

9. Catarina had a total of $2.00. This money consisted of the same number of nickels, dimes, and quarters. How many of each did she have?

10. What is the 200th letter in the sequence A, B, C, D, E, F, A, B C, D, E, F, ...?

11. Gerald and Betty each ran 5 blocks on one day. They then began increasing their runs by 3 blocks each day until they were running 35 blocks each. How many days did it take to do this?

12. Place the digits 2, 3, 4, 5, and 6 in the squares below to obtain the product shown.

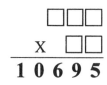

13. How many numbers are there between 100 and 1000 that contain the digits 7, 8, or 9?

14. Solve the following for x.
    (a) $5x - 17 = 33$

    (b) $5(x - 1) = 3x + 1$

15. Translate the following into an algebraic expression or an algebraic equation. Take any number. Divide it by 3. Subtract 7. Multiply the result by 14 and the answer is 11.

16. Choose one problem solving strategy and write a problem that could be solved with the strategy identified.

*17. Which of the following are statements?
    _____ (a)   William Jefferson Clinton is bald.

    _____ (b) $x - 3 = 3 - x$

*18. Negate each of the following:
    (a)   Reading a book each day will make you a wise person.

    (b)   All numbers are natural numbers.

*19. Consider the following statement: If Missoula is in Montana, then it is in the Northwest. Write each of the following:

(a)   The converse of the statement.

(b)   The contrapositive of the statement.

(c)   The inverse of the statement.

*20. Find a valid conclusion for the following argument:
If a person is a senior in college, then he has completed all of his general education requirements.
Jackson is a senior in college.

1. (a) 127, 107, 147
    (b) 6250, 31250, 156250
    (c) 43, 50, 57
    (d) 32, 0, 64
    (e) 25, 29, 33

2. (a) neither
    (b) geometric with common ratio of 5
    (c) arithmetic with common difference of 7
    (d) neither
    (e) arithmetic with common difference of 4

3. (a) $4 + (n-1)5$ or $5n - 1$

    (b) $6 \cdot 2^{(n-1)}$
    (c) n^2

4. (a) 11, 15, 19, 23, 27
    (b) 3, 8, 15, 24, 35
    (c) 0, 2, 6, 12, 20

5. 1218

6. 9

7. The test tube will overflow on the 12th night. At the end of the first night the test tube contains 25 mL, but by the end of the first day it contains only 16 mL. The net gain after one night and one day is 16 mL. If the test tube has more than 175 mL at nightfall, it will over flow during the night. After the 11th night and day the test tube contains 11 • 16 or 176 mL. Therefore, it will overflow the following night.

8. 47 posts. To solve this problem, count the number of posts in each side of the rectangle, but make sure that you count each corner post only once. One of the 120-ft sides has a post every 10 ft. That means there are 13 posts on that side.

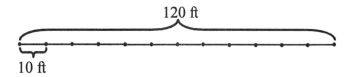

120 ft

10 ft

Note that two of the thirteen posts are corner posts. Similarly, the other 120-ft side has 16 posts and the two 80-ft sides have 11 posts each. Each corner post is in two sides, so we have counted the corner posts twice. So, we need to subtract 4. Therefore, we have $13 + 16 + 11 + 11 - 4 = 47$ posts.

9. Caterina had 5 of each coin.

10. B. There are six letters that repeat. So the seventh letter in the sequence is one complete repetition plus one letter, so it is an 'A.' The 16th letter in the sequence is two complete repetitions plus four letters, so it is a 'D.' Similarly, the 200th letter in the sequence is 33 complete repetitions plus two letters, so it is a 'B.'

11. Each ran 35 blocks on the 11th day.

12.   465
     x 23
    10695

13. 606

14. (a) 10
    (b) 3

15. Let n be any number. The equation becomes

$$\left(\frac{n}{3} - 7\right)14 = 11$$

16. The answers will vary depending on the strategy chosen.

*17. (a) Statement
     (b) Not a statement

*18. (a) Reading a book each day will not make you a wise person.
     (b) Some numbers are not natural numbers.

*19. (a) If Missoula is in the Northwest, it is in Montana.
     (b) If Missoula is not in the Northwest, it is not in Montana.
     (c) If Missoula is not in Montana, it is not in the Northwest.

*20. Jackson has completed all of his general education requirements.

Sample Assessment

1. List all the subsets of $\{2, o, t\}$.

2. Let $U = \{x \mid x \text{ is a female}\}$
       $A = \{x \mid x \text{ is a mathematician}\}$
       $B = \{x \mid x \text{ owns a pickup}\}$
       $C = \{x \mid x \text{ owns a dog}\}$

    Describe in words a member of each of the following:

    (a) $\overline{B}$

    (b) $B \cup C$

    (c) $A - C$

    (d) $\overline{A \cup C}$

    (e) $B - A$

    (f) $\overline{A}$

3. Let $U = \{u, n, i, t, e\}$
       $A = \{n, i, t\}$
       $B = \{n, e\}$
       $C = \{u, n, i, t, e\}$
       $D = \{u, e\}$

    Find each of the following:

    (a) $A \cap B$
    (b) $C \cup D$
    (c) $\overline{D}$
    (d) $\overline{A \cup D}$
    (e) $B \cap \overline{C}$
    (f) $(B \cap C) \cap D$
    (g) $(A \cap B) \cap (C \cup D)$
    (h) $(C - D) \cap \overline{A}$
    (i) $n(C)$
    (j) $n(C \cup D)$

4.   Indicate the following sets by shading.

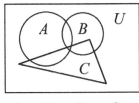

(a) $(A \cup B) \cup C$

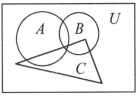

(b) $A \cap (B \cup C)$

5.   Let $C = \{p, l, u, s\}$. How many proper subsets does C have?

6.   How many possible one-to-one correspondences are there between sets D and E if $D = \{w, h, y\}$ and $E = \{n, o, t\}$?

7.   How many elements are there in the Cartesian product of sets D and E in Problem 6?

8.   Use a Venn diagram to determine whether $A \cup (B - C) = (B \cup A) - C$ for all sets A, B, and C.

9.   Describe using symbols, the shaded portion in each of the following:

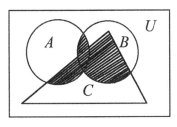

(a)

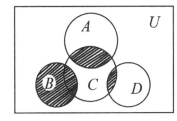

(b)

10. Classify each of the following as true or false. If false, tell why or give an example showing that it is not true.

    (a)   For all sets A and B, $A - B = B - A$

    (b)   For all sets A, $\emptyset \subseteq A$

    (c)   For all sets A, $A \subseteq A \cup \emptyset$

    (d)   The set $\{r, s, t, \ldots, z\}$ is a finite set.

    (e)   No set can be equivalent to all of its subsets,

11. In an interview of 50 math majors,
    12 liked calculus and geometry
    18 liked calculus but not algebra
    4 liked calculus, algebra, and geometry
    25 liked calculus
    15 liked geometry
    10 liked algebra but neither calculus nor geometry
    2 liked geometry and algebra but not calculus.
    Of those surveyed, how many liked calculus and algebra?

12. For each of the following, identify the whole-number properties that are illustrated.

    (a) $2(3 + 4) = 2(4 + 3)$

    (b) $5 + 7 = 7 + 5$

    (c) $1 \cdot 14 = 14 = 14 \cdot 1$

    (d) $5(9 + 3) = 5 \cdot 9 + 5 \cdot 3$

    (e) $2 + (3 + 2) = (2 + 3) + 2$

    (f) $5(3 \cdot 4) = (5 \cdot 3)4$

13. Using the definition of less than or greater than, prove that each of the following inequalities is true.

    (a) $5 < 7$

    (b) $18 > 14$

14. For each of the following, find all possible whole-number replacements that make the following statements true.

    (a) $5 \cdot \square + 27 < 48$

    (b) $944 = \square \cdot 48 + 32$

    (c) $28 - \square \geq 14$

15. Use the distributive property of multiplication over addition and addition and subtraction facts to rename each of the following, if possible.

    (a) $2x + 4x + 7x + 5x$

    (b) $6x^3 + 7x^3$

    (c) $a(b + c + d)$

16. Jim was paid $800 a month for his first 6 months of work and then received a $20 per month raise for his next 6 months. How much money did he make for the year?

17. Sue argued that $0 \div 0 = 1$ because any number divided by itself is 1. What would you tell her?

18.   If q and r are whole numbers such that $109 = 5q - r$ and $0 < r < 5$, find q and r.

19.   Assuming that a, b and $a \div b$ are whole numbers and $b \neq 0$, explain why $(a \div b) \cdot b = a$.

20.   Which of the following sets are functions from the set of first components to the set of second components?

(a) $\{(b, a), (d, c), (a, e), (g, f)\}$

(b) $\{(a, b), (b, a), (c, c), (a, c)\}$

(c) $\{(b, a), (c, a), (b, b), (c, b)\}$

21.   Given the following function rules and domains, find the associated ranges.

(a) $f(x) = 5x + 3$, Domain = $\{0, 1, 2, 3, 4\}$

(b) $f(x) = x^2 - 1$, Domain = $\{1, 9, 4\}$

(c) $f(x) = 2x + x^2$, Domain = $\{1, 0, 2\}$

22.   If $f(x) = 3x - 10$, find the element of the domain associated with each of the following functional values:

(a)   2

(b)   8

23. Consider a function machine that accepts inputs as ordered pairs. Suppose the components of the ordered pairs are natural numbers and the first component is the length of the rectangle and the second is its width. The following machine computes the area of the rectangle. Thus for a rectangle whose length, ℓ, is 3 and whose width w, is 2, the input is (3,2) and the output is $3 \cdot 2$ or 6. Answer each of the following.

   (a)   For each of the following inputs, find the corresponding outputs: (3,4), (4,3), (6,2), (1,12).

   (b)   Find the set of all the inputs for which the output is 20.

   (c)   What is the domain and the range of the function?

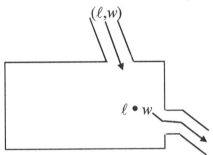

24. The following graphs show the cost and revenue functions in dollars for producing cameras From the graphs estimate the following.

   (a)   The break-even point—that is, the number of cameras that must be sold to meet expenses exactly.
   (b)   The profit or loss on the first 25 cameras produced and sold.
   (c)   The number of cameras that must be sold to gain a $2000 profit.

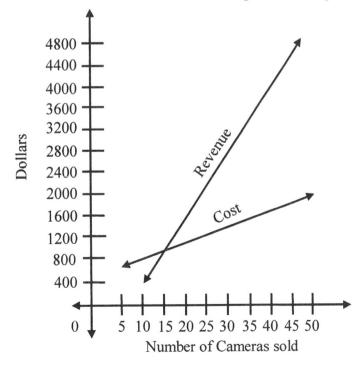

1. $\varnothing$, {2}, {*o*}, {2, *o*}, {*t*}, {2, *t*}, {*o, t*}, {2, *o, t*}

2.   (a)   *x* is a female who does not own a pickup.
     (b)   *x* is a female who either owns a pickup or a dog or both.
     (c)   *x* is a female mathematician who does not own a dog.
     (d)   *x* is a female nonmathematician who does not own a dog.
     (e)   *x* is a female who owns a pickup but is not a mathematician.
     (f)   *x* is a female nonmathematician.

3.   (a)   {*n*}   (b)   {*u, n, i, t, e*} or *C* or *U* (c)   {*n, i, t*} or *A*
     (d) $\varnothing$ (e) $\varnothing$ (f)   {*e*}
     (g)   {*n*}   (h) $\varnothing$ (i)   5
     (j)   5

4.   (a)   (b)

   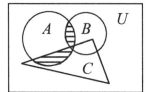

5.   15

6.   6

7.   9

8.

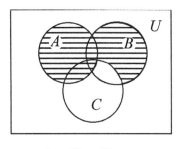   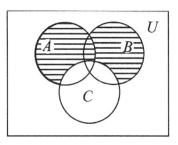

     $A \cup (B - C)$ $\neq$ $(B \cup A) - C$

9.   Answers may vary. For example,

     (a) $(A \cap B) \cup (A \cap C) \cup (B \cap C)$
     (b) $(A \cap C) \cup (D \cap C) \cup B$

10. (a) False; Let $A = \{1, 2\}$ and $B = \{1\}$.
    (b) True
    (c) True
    (d) True
    (e) False; The empty set is equivalent to itself.

11. 7

12. (a) Commutative Property of Addition
    (b) Commutative Property for Addition
    (c) Multiplicative Identity
    (d) Distributive Property of Multiplication over Addition
    (e) Associative Property of Addition
    (f) Associative Property for Multiplication

13. (a) Let $k = 2$. Since $2 + 5 = 7$, then $5 < 7$.
    (b) Let $k = 4$. Since $18 = 4 + 14$, then $18 > 14$.

14. (a) $\{0, 1, 2, 3, 4\}$ (b) $\{19\}$ (c) $\{0, 1, 2, ..., 14\}$

15. (a) $18x$ (b) $13x^3$ (c) $ab + ac + ad$

16. $10,020

17. $0 \div 0$ is defined then it must equal to some unique number x such that $0 = 0 \cdot x$. Because no unique whole number exists, $0 \div 0$ has no meaning.

18 $q = 21$, $r = 4$

19. By definition of division in terms of multiplication, $a \div b = c$ if $a = c \cdot b$.
20. Substituting $a \div b$ for c in the last equation we have: $a = (a \div b) \cdot b$.

20. (a) Yes   (b) No   (c) No

21. (a) $\{3, 8, 13, 18, 23\}$
    (b) $\{0, 80, 15\}$
    (c) $\{3, 0, 8\}$

22. (a) 4   (b) 6

23. (a) Each output is 12
    (b) $\{(1, 20), (20, 1), (2, 10), (10, 2), (4, 5), (5, 4)\}$
    (c) If N is the set of natural numbers, then the domain is $N \times N$ and the range is N.

24. (a) 15   (b) $1200   (c) 32

Sample Assessment

1. Write the set $M = \{1, 3, 5, 7, 9\}$ using set-builder notation.

2. List all the nonempty proper subsets of $\{a, b, c\}$.

3. Let $U = \{x \mid x \text{ is an American}\}$
    $C = \{x \mid x \text{ is a smoker}\}$
    $D = \{x \mid x \text{ is a health problem}\}$
    $E = \{x \mid x \text{ is a male}\}$

    (a)   Describe a person who is an element of each of the following sets:

    (i) $\overline{C}$

    (ii) $\overline{C} \cap \overline{D}$

    (iii) $C \cap D$

    (iv) $D - C$

    (v) $D \cup C$

    (b)   Use the sets above, along with the set operations to describe a set of which each of the following is a representative member.

    (i)   A healthy American Male

    (ii)   An unhealthy male smoker

    (iii) A nonsmoking healthy female

    (iv)   An American who is either a female or a nonsmoker

4. Classify the following as true or false, where A and B are any two sets. If false, give a counterexample.

   (a) $A \cup B = A$, then $B \subseteq A$

   (b)   If $A \subseteq B$, then $A \cup B = B$

   (c) $(A \cup B) \cup C = A \cup (B \cup C)$

   (d) $A \cap \overline{A} = \varnothing$

   (e) $A \cup \overline{A} = \varnothing$

   (f) $A - \overline{A} = \varnothing$

   (g) $A \times \overline{A} = U$

   (h) $\varnothing \subset \varnothing$

5. If $U = \{q, u, e, s, t\}$, $A = \{s, e, t\}$, $B = \{s, u, e\}$, and $C = \{q, u\}$, find each of the following:

   (a) $A \cup B$ (b) $A \cap \overline{C}$

   (c) $A \cup \overline{(B \cap C)}$ (d) $\overline{A} \cap \overline{B}$

   (e) $A - B$ (f) $(A \cup B) \cap (A \cup C)$

   (g) $A \cup \overline{A}$ (h) $n(B - A)$

6. Let $A = \{1, 2\}$ and $B = \{a\}$. Find the following:

   (a) $n(A \times B)$

   (b) $n(B \times A)$

   (c) $B \times B$

   (d) $A \times A$

   (e) $\varnothing \times A$

   (f) Is $A \times A$ a function from A to A?

   (g) Is $B \times B$ a function from B to B?

   (h) $n(A \times \varnothing)$

7. (a) Illustrate a one-to-one correspondence between the following sets:

   $$N = \{1, 2, 3, 4, \ldots, n, \ldots\}$$

   $$F = \{4, 9, 14, 19, 24, \ldots\}$$

   (b) In your correspondence, what element of F corresponds to 57? Explain why.

   (c) In your correspondence, what element of F corresponds to n?

8. Given the function rules and domains, find the associated ranges.

   (a) $f(x) = 2x + 3$, domain $= \{0, 1, 2\}$

   (b) $f(x) = 0$, domain $= \{0, 1, 2\}$

9. Shade the Venn diagram to illustrate $\overline{A} \cup \overline{B}$.

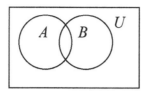

10. Describe in symbols the shaded portion Venn diagram below.

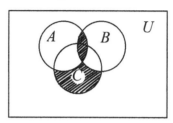

11. A survey was made of 200 students to study their use of the public library system. The findings were as follows:

    60 used the Reader's Guide.
    28 used both the card catalog and the information booth.
    68 used the information booth.
    83 did not use the library.
    43 used only the card catalog.

    Explain how the above information can be used to conclude that some students must use both the information booth and the Reader's Guide.

12. If there are 36 different flavors of ice cream and two types of cones are available, how many choice for a single scoop of ice cream on some type of cone do you have?

13. If $A = \{a, b, c, d\}$ and $B = \{1, 2, 3, 4\}$, how many different one-to-one correspondences can be made?

14. Which of the following sets are functions from the set of first components to the set of second component?

    (a) $\{(1, 2), (2, 1)\}$

    (b) $\{(5, 10), (10, 10), (15, 10), (20, 10)\}$

15. If $f(x) = x - 1$, $g(x) = x + 1$, and $N = \{1, 2, 3, 4,...\}$ is the domain of each function, find the simplest possible expression for the following.

    (a) $f(g(x))$

    (b) $g(f(x))$

16. The following graphs show the cost and revenue functions in dollars for producing dishwashers. From the graphs estimate the following.

    (a)   The break-even point—that is, the number of dishwashers that must be sold to meet expenses exactly.
    (b)   The number of units that must be sold to gain a $6000 profit.

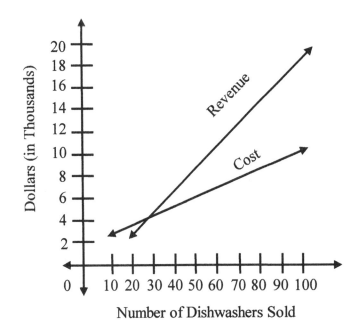

Number of Dishwashers Sold

17. Using the definition of less than or greater than, prove each of the following is true.

    (a) $18 < 22$

    (b) $1 > 0$

18. For each of the following, find all possible whole-number replacements that make the following statements true.

    (a) $2 \cdot \square + 15 < 27$

    (b) $123 = 7 \cdot 17 + \square$

19. Use the distributive property of multiplication over addition and addition and subtraction facts to rename each of the following, if possible.

    (a) $5x^2 + 2x^2 + 7x^2$

    (b) $8x + 9x + 11x + 9x$

    (c) $(a + b)(c + d)$.

20. I am thinking of a number. If I add 3, multiply the result by 15 and then subtract 25, I get 200. What is my number?

21. Use the definition of division to show that for all whole numbers a and b where
    $b \neq 0, (a \cdot b) \div b = a$

1. $M = \{x \mid x \text{ is an odd natural number less than } 11\}$

2. $\{a\}, \{b\}, \{c\}, \{a, b\}, \{a, c\}, \{b, c\}$

3.   (a)   (i)   A nonsmoking American
        (ii)   A healthy nonsmoking American
        (iii) An American smoker with a health problem
        (iv)   An American nonsmoker with a health problem
        (v)   An American who is either a smoker or unhealthy or both

     (b)   (i) $\overline{D} \cap E$
        (ii) $D \cap E \cap C$
        (iii) $\overline{C} \cap \overline{D} \cap \overline{E}$
        (iv) $\overline{E} \cup \overline{C}$

4.   (a)   T   (b)   T   (c)   T
     (d)   T   (e)   F. $A \cup \overline{A} = U$ (f)   F. $A - \overline{A} = A$
     (g)   F. Let $A = \{1\}$, and $U = \{1, 2\}$. Then $\overline{A} = \{2\}$ and $A \times \overline{A} = \{(1, 2)\}$.
     (h)   F. $\varnothing \subseteq \varnothing$

5.   (a) $\{s, u, e, t\}$ (b) $\{s, e, t\}$, or A
     (c) $\{q, e, s, t\}$ (d) $\{q\}$
     (e) $\{t\}$ (f) $\{s, u, e, t\}$
     (g) U (h)   1

6.   (a)   2   (b)   2
     (c) $B \times B = \{(a, a)\}$ (d) $A \times A = \{(1, 1), (1, 2), (2, 1), (2, 2)\}$
     (e) $\varnothing$ (f)   No
     (g)   Yes   (h)   0

7.   (a) $\{1, \quad 2, \quad 3, \quad 4, \quad \ldots, \quad n, \quad \ldots\}$
        $\{4, \quad 9, \quad 14, \quad 19, \quad \ldots, \quad 5n-1, \quad \ldots\}$
     (b)   284, because $5(57) - 1 = 284$
     (c) $5n - 1$

8.   (a) $\{3, 5, 7\}$ (b) $\{0\}$

9.
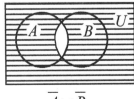

$\overline{A} \cup \overline{B}$

10. $(A \cap B) \cup [C - (A \cup B)]$

11. Use a Venn Diagram as shown below, where C represents card catalog users, R represents Reader's Guide users, and I represents the users of the information booth.

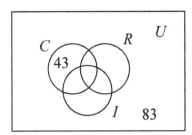

If there was no overlap between the users of the information booth and the Reader's Guide, we would have the following: $n(R) + n(I) + 43 + 83 = 200$. Thus, $n(R) + n(I) = 74$, but $n(R) = 60$ and $n(I) = 68$. Since $60 + 68 \neq 74$, there must be an overlap.

12. 72

13. $4 \cdot 3 \cdot 2 \cdot 1 = 24$

14. (a) Yes
    (b) Yes.

15. (a) $f(g(x)) = x$ (b) $g(f(x)) = x$

16. (a) 30   (b) 80 units

17. (a) Let $k = 4$. Since $18 + 4 = 22$, then $18 < 22$.
    (b) Let $k = 1$. Since $0 + 1 = 1$, then $1 > 0$.

18. (a) $\{0, 1, 2, 3, 4, 5\}$ (b) 4.

19. (a) $14x^2$ (b) $37x$ (c) $ac + ad + bc + bd$

20. 12

21. By definition of division $(a \cdot b) \div b = x$ if and only if the equation $ab = bx$ has a unique solution. Because $x = a$ is the unique solution, the result follows.

Sample Assessment

1. Name two properties that the Roman system has that the Egyptian system did not have.

2. Write the first fifteen counting numbers in base four.

3. Write the number preceding and succeeding each of the following.

    (a) EET_{twelve} _____   _____

    (b) 10011_{two} _____   _____

4. Write each of the following in the indicated base.

    (a) 1011_{two} to base ten.   _____

    (b) 1574 to base twelve   _____

    (c) MCMLIV to base ten _____

5. If $2b_{six} = 17_{eight}$, what is the value of b?   _____

6. Identify the whole number property illustrated in each of the following.

    (a) $4 + (7 + 3) = 4 + (3 + 7)$ _____

    (b) $5 \cdot 1 = 5$ _____

    (c) $5 \cdot (5 \cdot 6) = (5 \cdot 5) \cdot 6$ _____

    (d) $4 \cdot (5 + 6) = (4 \cdot 5) + (4 \cdot 6)$ _____

    (e) $4 + 5$ is a whole number   _____

7. Explain whether the set $\{0, 1, 2\}$ is closed with respect to addition on whole numbers.

8. Find the missing numbers in each of the following:

(a)
```
   5 _ 4
 _ 3 2 6
 ─────────
   _ 4 8
```

(b)
```
     1 4 6
   _   6 _
   + 3 _ 8
   ─────────
   1 0 3 5
```

9. Simplify each of the following, if possible. Write your answers in the exponential form a^b.

(a) $2^4 \cdot 2^5 \cdot 2^8$ _____   (b) $3^4 + 2 \cdot 3^4$ _____   (c) $2^{50} \cdot 2^{50}$ _____

10. Use scratch arithmetic to perform the following operation.

34_{five}
42_{five}
33_{five}
24_{five}
$+ 43_{five}$

11. Multiply $234 \cdot 57$ using lattice multiplication. Show all work.

12. Perform the following operations.

(a) 1034_{five}
$\quad +344_{five}$

(b) 10001_{two}
$\quad - 1011_{two}$

(c) 103_{five}
$\quad \times 23_{five}$

(d) $11_{two} \overline{)1111}_{two}$

13. Explain how you would use front-end estimation to get an estimate for the following.

585
422
310
$+796$

14. For each of the following base-ten numbers, tell the place value of the underlined numbers.

(a) 5<u>2</u>86 _____   (b) 843<u>3</u> _____   (c) 34<u>5</u>6 _____

15. Tell how to use compatible numbers to compute each of the following.

(a) $122 + 13 + 78 + 37 + 9$

(b) $4 \cdot 8 \cdot 20 \cdot 25$

16. Explain why the scratch arithmetic algorithm works.

17. Place the digits 2, 4, 5, 6, and 8 in the boxes to obtain

(a)   the greatest difference   □ □ □
                                  – □ □

(b)   the greatest product   □ □ □
                              x □ □

18. Hugo's checking account at the beginning of the month had a balance of $250. During the month he wrote five checks for $15, two checks for $12, and one check for $107. He made one deposit for $62. What is his new balance? _____

19. Jim was paid $800 a month for his first six months of work and then received a $20 per month raise for his next six months. How much money did he make for the year? _____

20. Tom, Dick, and Mary decided to share expenses for a class party. Tom bought $28 worth of pizza, Dick bought $20 worth of ice cream, and Mary bought $15 worth of soft drinks. How much should each person pay in order that each of them spend the same amount of money and how might they accomplish this?

1. The Roman system has a multiplicative property and a subtractive property.

2. $(1, 2, 3, 10, 11, 12, 13, 20, 21, 22, 23, 30, 31, 32, 33)_{four}$

3. (a) $EE9_{twelve}$, EEE_{twelve} (b) 10010_{two}, 10100_{two}

4. (a) 11   (b) $TE2_{twelve}$ (c) 1954

5. 3

6. (a) Commutative Property of Addition
   (b) Identity Property for Multiplication
   (c) Associative Property for Multiplication
   (d) Distributive Property of Multiplication over Addition
   (e) Closure Property of Addition

7. No, $2 + 2 = 4$ and 4 is not an element of the set.

8. (a)   574
       $- 326$
         248

   (b)   146
         561
       $+ 328$
       1035

9. (a) 2^{17} (b) 3^{5} (c) 2^{100}

10.
      $^{3}\not{4}$ 4 $_{five}$
     $\not{4}_{0}\not{2}_{1}$ $_{five}$
      3 3 $_{five}$
     $\not{2}_{0}\not{4}_{3}$ $_{five}$
   $+$ 4 $\not{3}_{1}$ $_{five}$
     3 4 1 $_{five}$

11.

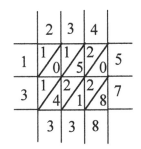

12. (a) 1433_{five} (b) 110_{two} (c) 2424_{five} (d) 101_{two}

13. $5 + 3 + 3 + 7 = 18$ so the first estimate is 1800. $85 + 22$ is about 100 and $96 + 10$ is about 100 so the adjustment is 200. Therefore the final estimate is $1800 + 200 = 2000$.

14. (a) hundreds   (b) units or ones   (c) tens

15. (a) $122 + 78 = 200$ and $13 + 37 = 50$ so the sum is $200 + 50 + 9 = 259$.

   (b) $4 \cdot 25 = 100$ and $8 \cdot 20 = 160$ so the product is $160 \cdot 100 = 16,000$.

16. Answers vary, for example, the scratch marks represent the normal carries and the scratches are just one way to keep track of them.

17. (a) $\begin{array}{r} 865 \\ -\ 24 \\ \hline 841 \end{array}$ (b) $\begin{array}{r} 652 \\ \times\ 84 \\ \hline 54,768 \end{array}$

18. $106

19. $9720

20. One possibility is that Dick should pay Tom $1 and Mary should pay Tom $6.

Sample Assessment

1. Name two properties that the Roman system has that Hindu Arabic system does not have.

2. Write the first fifteen counting numbers in base six.

3. Write the number preceding and succeeding each of the following.

    (a) $E0E_{twelve}$ _____   _____

    (b) 10101_{two} _____   _____

4. Write each of the following in the indicated base.

    (a) 1021_{three} to base ten. _____

    (b) 534 to base twelve _____

    (c) MCMLXII to base ten _____

5. If $12_b = 13_{five}$, what number base b is being used? _____

6. Identify the property of whole numbers illustrated in each of the following.

    (a) $4 + (7 + 3) = (4 + 7) + 3$ _____

    (b) $5 + 0 = 5$ _____

    (c) $5 \cdot (5 \cdot 6) = 5 \cdot (6 \cdot 5)$ _____

    (d) $4 \cdot (5 + 6) = (4 \cdot 5) + (4 \cdot 6)$ _____

    (e) $4 \cdot 5$ is a whole number   _____

7. Explain whether the set {2, 4, 6, 8, 10, 12, ... } is closed with respect to addition on whole numbers.

8.   Find the missing numbers in each of the following:

(a)
$$
\begin{array}{r}
- \; - \; - \\
- \quad 7 \; 6 \\
\hline
1 \; 4 \; 9
\end{array}
$$

(b)
$$
\begin{array}{r}
2 \; \_ \; 4 \\
\_ \; 6 \; \_ \\
+ \; 8 \; 1 \; 4 \\
\hline
1 \; 6 \; 1 \; 0
\end{array}
$$

9.   Simplify each of the following, if possible. Write your answers in the form a^b.

(a) $5^4 \cdot 5^7 \cdot 5^9$ _____   (b) $5^4 + 4 \cdot 5^4$ _____   (c) $2^{10} \cdot 2^{15}$ _____

10. Use scratch arithmetic to perform the following operation.

$$
\begin{array}{r}
23_{\text{four}} \\
12_{\text{four}} \\
33_{\text{four}} \\
22_{\text{four}} \\
+ \; 32_{\text{four}} \\
\end{array}
$$

11. Multiply $523 \cdot 73$ using lattice multiplication. Show all work.

12. Perform the following operations.

(a) 1434_{five} (b) 10101_{two} (c) 434_{five} (d) $14_{\text{five}}\overline{)332}_{\text{five}}$

$+343_{\text{five}}$ -1011_{two} $\text{x } 32_{\text{five}}$

13. Explain how you would use front-end estimation to get an estimate for the following.

$$
\begin{array}{r}
575 \\
22 \\
305 \\
+796 \\
\end{array}
$$

14. For each of the following base-ten numbers, tell the place value of the underlined numbers.

(a) 325<u>6</u> _____   (b) <u>6</u>25 _____   (c) <u>5</u>123 _____

15. Tell how to use compatible numbers to compute each of the following.

(a) $125 + 3 + 40 + 37 + 75 + 60$

(b) $4 \cdot 4 \cdot 50 \cdot 25$

16. Is the front-end estimate of a sum always less than or equal to the actual estimate? Explain why or why not.

17. If 10 is removed from the set of whole numbers, is the set closed with respect to addition? Explain why or why not?

18. Joyce sold 48 student tickets to the play at $3.00 each and 37 adult tickets at $5.00 each. Expenses for the play were $300. How much money was left in the account after expenses were paid. _____

19. I am thinking of a number. If I add 3, multiply the result by 15 and then subtract 25, I get 200. What is my number? _____

20. Sam's operating expenses for driving a car are $40 per week. If his expenses for driving a motorcycle for 52 weeks are $1650, how much did he save for the 52-week period?

_____

1. The Roman system has a multiplicative property and a subtractive property.

2. $(1, 2, 3, 4, 5, 10, 11, 12, 13, 14, 15, 20, 21, 22, 23)_{six}$

3. (a) EOT_{twelve}, $E10_{twelve}$ (b) 10100_{two}, 10110_{two}

4. (a) 34   (b) 386_{twelve} (c) 1962

5. 6

6. (a) Associative Property of Addition
   (b) Identity Property for Addition
   (c) Commutative Property of Multiplication
   (d) Distributive Property of Multiplication over Addition
   (e) Closure Property of Multiplication

7. It is closed with respect to addition because the sum of two even numbers is an even number. If $n \in W$, then $2n$ is even. Also, $2n + 2n = 4n = 2(2n)$, so the sum is always even.

8. (a)
$$\begin{array}{r} 225 \\ -\ 76 \\ \hline 149 \end{array}$$
   (b)
$$\begin{array}{r} 234 \\ 562 \\ +\ 814 \\ \hline 1610 \end{array}$$

9. (a) 5^{20} (b) 5^5 (c) 2^{25}

10.
$$\begin{array}{r} {}^3\!\not{2}_1\ 3 \ _{four} \\ 1\ \not{2}_1 \ _{four} \\ \not{3}_1\ \not{3}_0 \ _{four} \\ 2\ 2 \ _{four} \\ +\ \not{3}_2\ \not{2}_0 \ _{four} \\ \hline 3\ 2\ 0 \ _{four} \end{array}$$

11.

12. (a) 2332_{five} (b) 1010_{two} (c) 31043_{five} (d) $(20 \text{ R } 2)_{five}$

13. $5 + 3 + 7 = 15$ so the first estimate is 1500. $75 + 22$ is about 100 and $96 + 5$ is about 100 so the adjustment is 200. Therefore the final estimate is $1500 + 200 = 1700$.

14. (a) ones or units   (b) hundreds   (c) thousands

15. (a) $125 + 75 = 200$ and $60 + 40 = 100$ so the sum is $200 + 100 + 9 = 259$.

    (b) $4 \cdot 25 = 100$ and $8 \cdot 20 = 160$ so the product is $160 \cdot 100 = 16,000$.

16. Yes, because the adjustment has not yet been made and the adjustment is added to the front-end estimate. The least that the adjustment could be is 0.

17. No, for example $3 + 7 = 10$ and if 10 does not belong to the set, than the set is not closed.

18. $29

19. $12

20. $430

Sample Assessment

1. For each of the following, find all integer values of x that make the equation or inequality true.

    (a) $x^2 = 9$

    (b) $|{}^-x| = 5$

    (c) $4 - 3x < 2x + 84$

    (d) $|x + 2| = 7$

    (e) $x + 7 = 34 - 2x$

    (f) $(x - 3)^2 = 64$

2. Use a pattern approach to explain why $(-3) \cdot (4) = -12$.

3. Factor each of the following expressions.

    (a) $5x - 3x^2$

    (b) $25 - x^2$

4. Evaluate the following when $x = -3$, if possible.

    (a) $-x$

    (b) $|x|$

    (c) $-x^2$

    (d) ${}^-(1 + x)$

5. Use the formula $(a - b)(a + b) = a^2 - b^2$ to multiply each of the following and simplify your answer.

(a) $(b + 3d)(b - 3d)$

(b) $(-4j + 2k)(-4j - 2k)$

6. Classify each of the following as true or false, where a and b are any integers. If false, tell why.

(a) If $ac > bc$, then $a > b$.   (b)   If $-x > {}^-7$, then $x > 7$.

(c) $|x|$ is always equal to x.   (d) $a^2 + b^2 = (a + b)(a + b)$

7. The temperature dropped 15 degrees from the high temperature to $-6°$ C. What was the high temperature? _____

8. The sum of two integers is 14. Their difference is 8. What are the integers? _____

9. Demonstrate the addition $^-5 + {}^-3 = {}^-8$ using each of the following models:
    (a) Number line   (b)   Charged field

10. Determine all possible digits to fill in the blanks to make each of the following true.
    (a) $9 | 482\_\_$ (b) $6 | 24\_\_35$ (c) $4 | 63\_\_$

_____   _____   _____

11. Classify each of the following as true or false, where a and b are integers. If false, give a counterexample.

(a) If $a \neq b$, then $GCD(a, b) = 1$.

(b) If a and b are even, then $GCD(a, b) = 2$.

(c) If $a \mid b$, then $LCM(a, b) = a$.

(d) If $6 \mid a$ then $12 \mid a$.

12. Find the least whole number with exactly seven positive divisors and explain why it is the least.

13. Determine whether each of the following numbers is prime or composite.

(a) 219   (b) 791   (c) 1001

14. Find each of the following.

(a) $GCD(12, 26, 65)$

(b) $LCM(12, 26, 65)$

15. If $a = 2^3 \cdot 3^7 \cdot 5^3 \cdot 11^4$ and $b = 2^2 \cdot 3^5 \cdot 7^2 \cdot 11 \cdot 13$, find the following. (Leave your answer written with exponents).

   (a) GCD(a, b)

   (b) LCM(a,b)

16. Describe a divisibility test for 35.

17. Jane cut her cake into 6 pieces of equal size. Lori cut her cake into 8 pieces of equal size. If the cakes must now be cut so that they are identical, into how many pieces should each cake be cut?

18. In their freshman years, Jacqueline took 43 credit hours and Jean took 47 credit hours. If Jacqueline took only 5-credit courses and Jean took only 3-credit courses after their freshman years, how many credits did they have when they had the same number?

*19. Christmas falls on Monday this year. On what day will it fall next year if next year is a leap year?

*20. Find the remainder when 7^{100} is divided by 9.

1. (a)   3, $^-$3   (b)   5, $^-$5   (c) $x > {}^-16, x \in I$

    (d)   5, $^-$9   (e)   9   (f)   11, $^-$5

2. $2 \cdot 4 = 8$ The first three products 8, 4, 0 are terms of an arithmetic
    $1 \cdot 4 = 4$ sequence with fixed difference $^-$4. If the pattern continues
    $0 \cdot 4 = 0$ the next three terms are $^-$4, $^-$8 and $^-$12.
    $^-1 \cdot 4 = {}^-4$
    $^-2 \cdot 4 = {}^-8$
    $^-3 \cdot 4 = {}^-12$

3. (a) $x(5 - 3x)$ (b) $(5 - x)(5 + x)$

4. (a)   3   (b)   3   (c) $^-$9   (d)   2

5. (a) $b^2 - 9d^2$ (b) $16j^2 - 4k^2$

6. (a)   F. Counterexample: $2(^-1) > 7(^-1)$ and $2 < 7$.
    (b)   F. If $^-x > {}^-7$, then $(^-1)(^-x) < (^-1)(^-7)$, or $x < 7$.
    (c)   F. Counterexample: $x = {}^-2$
    (d)   F. $(a + b)(a + b) = a^2 + 2ab + b^2$

7. 9° C

8. 11 and 3

9. (a)

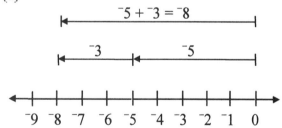

(b)

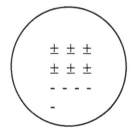

$^-$5 charge on field

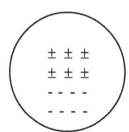

Add three negative charges;
net result is $^-$8 charge on field

10. (a) 4   (b)   None   (c)   2 or 6

11. (a) F. Let $a = 4$ and $b = 8$.   (b)   F. Let $a = 4$ and $b = 8$.
    (c) F. Let $a = 4$ and $b = 8$.   (d)   F. Let $a = 6$.

12. 64 is the least whole number with exactly seven divisors because of the following:

    $$64 = 2^6$$

    2^6 has exactly 7 divisors: 1, 2, 4, 8, 16, 32, and 64.
    Every other positive number with 7 divisors must have some prime other than 2 in its prime factorization, and if it has a number greater than 2 in its prime factorization, then the number must be greater than 64.

13. (a) Composite   (b)   Composite   (c)   Composite

14. (a) 1   (b) $2^2 \cdot 3 \cdot 5 \cdot 13$ or 780

15. (a) $2^2 \cdot 3^5 \cdot 11$ (b) $2^3 \cdot 3^7 \cdot 5^3 \cdot 7^2 \cdot 11^4 \cdot 13$

16. For a number to be divisible by 35, it must be divisible by both 5 and 7.

17. 24 pieces

18. 53

19. Wednesday

20. 7

Sample Assessment

1. Explain why the additive inverse of $^-3 + x$ is $3 - x$.

2. For each of the following find all integer values of x, if they exist, that make the equations true.

   (a) $^-x - 3 = -8$

   (b) $x^3 = -27$

   (c) $|x| = 16$

   (d) $8 - 5x < 2x - 20$

   (e) $|^-x + 5| = 8$

   (f) $(x - 2)^4 = 16$

3. Factor each of the following expressions.

   (a) $9x^2 - 3x$

   (b) $4x^2 - 9$

4. (a) Use the Distributive Property of Multiplication over Addition to show that
        $(x + y)(x + y) = x^2 + 2xy + y^2$

   (b) Use the result in (a) to compute $(^-5 + 2a)(^-5 + 2a)$

5. Evaluate the following when $x = -2$, if possible.

   (a) $^-x^2$

   (b) $|^-x|$

   (c) $^-|x|$

   (d) x^3

6. Classify each of the following as true or false. If false, tell why.

   (a) If $^-x > 2$ then $x > ^-2$.

   (b) If $3x = 6$ then $^-6x = 12$.

   (c) $|^-x|$ is always equal to ^-x.

   (d) $a^2 - b^2 = (a - b)(a - b)$

7. Ann had a balance of $25 in her checking account. She wrote three checks for $5.00 each, one check for $28, and two checks for $22 each. What was her new balance?

8. The temperature dropped 37° C from the high temperature to reach a low of –8° C. What was the high temperature?

9. The difference between two integers is 22. The greater integer is equal to three times the smaller integer plus 8. What are the two integers?

10. Demonstrate $^-8 + 2 = ^-6$ using the following models:
    (a) Number line

10. (cont.)
     (b) Charged field

11. Determine all possible digits to fill in the blanks to make each of the following true.

     (a) $9 \mid 24\_3$ (b) $6 \mid 7\_4$ (c) $5 \mid 3728\_$

12. Classify each of the following as true or false where a and b are integers. If false, give a counterexample or tell why.

     (a) $GCD(a, a) = a$

     (b) If $LCM(a, b) = ab$, then $GCD(a, b) = 1$.

     (c) If $LCM(a, b) = 1$, then $a = 1$ and $b = 1$

     (d) If $6 \mid a$ and $2 \mid a$, then $12 \mid a$

13. Find the least whole number greater than 100 with exactly 3 divisors.

14. Determine whether each of the following numbers is prime or composite.

     (a)   231   (b)   393

15. Find each of the following.

    (a) GCD(156, 84, 292)

    (b) LCM(156, 84, 292)

16. If $a = 5^2 \cdot 7 \cdot 11 \cdot 13$ and $b = 2^3 \cdot 5^2 \cdot 7^3 \cdot 17$, find the following. (Leave your answer written with exponents).

    (a) GCD(a, b)   (b)   LCM(a,b)

17. Describe a divisibility test for 33.

18. Joel's dog barks every 9 minutes. Billy's dog barks every 15 minutes. They both barked at exactly 2:00 P.M. When is the next time they will bark at the same time?

*19. Christmas is on Tuesday this year. In how many years will it be on Friday if no leap years are involved?

*20. Find the remainder when 2^{64} is divided by 4.

1. Because $(^-3 + x) + (3 - x) = (^-3 + x) + (3 + ^-x) = (^-3 + 3) + (x + ^-x) = 0$

2. (a) 5   (b) $^-3$ (c) $16, ^-16$
   (d) $x > ^-4, x \in I$ (e) $^-3, 13$ (f) 0, 4

3. (a) $3x(3x - 1)$ (b) $(2x - 3)(2x + 3)$

4. (a) $(x + y)(x + y) = x(x + y) + y(x + y) = x^2 + xy + yx + y^2 = x^2 + 2xy + y^2$
   (b) $(^-5 + 2a)(^-5 + 2a) = (^-5)^2 + 2(^-5)(2a) + (2a)^2 = 25 - 20a + 4a^2$

5. (a) $^-4$ (b) 2   (c) $^-2$ (d) $^-8$

6. (a) F. $x < ^-2$ (b) F. $^-6x = ^-12$
   (c) F. $|^-x| = ^-x$ if $x \leq 0$ (d) F. $a^2 - b^2 = (a - b)(a + b)$

7. $^-\$62$

8. 29° C

9. 7 and 29

10. (a)

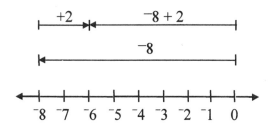

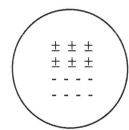

$^-8$ charge on field

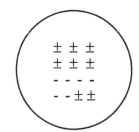

Add two positive charges;
net result is $^-6$ charge on field

(b)

11. (a) 0, 9   (b) 1, 4, 7   (c) 0, 5

12. (a) F. If $a = 0$, then there is no GCD.
    (b) T
    (c) T
    (d) F. Let $a = 6$.

13. 121

14. (a) Composite   (b) Composite

15. (a)   4   (b) $2^2 \cdot 3 \cdot 7 \cdot 13 \cdot 73$ or 79,716

16. (a) $5^2 \cdot 7$ (b) $2^3 \cdot 5^2 \cdot 7^3 \cdot 11 \cdot 13 \cdot 17$

17. A number is divisible by 33, if and only if it is divisible by both 3 and 11.

18. 2:45 P.M.

*19. 3 years

*20. 0

Sample Assessment

1. For each of the following, draw a diagram illustrating the fraction.

   (a) $\dfrac{1}{6}$ (b) $\dfrac{5}{7}$

2. Write three rational numbers equal to $\dfrac{4}{5}$. _____

3. Reduce each of the following rational numbers to simplest form.

   _____ (a) $\dfrac{36}{48}$

   _____ (b) $\dfrac{\left(cy^3\right)^2}{dy^2}$

   _____ (c) $\dfrac{0}{3}$

   _____ (d) $\dfrac{b^2+x}{b^3+bx}$

4. Place >, <, or = between each of the following pairs to make true sentences.

   _____ (a) $\dfrac{4}{5}$ and $\dfrac{120}{150}$

   _____ (b) $\dfrac{{}^-6}{5}$ and $\dfrac{{}^-7}{6}$

_____ (c) $\dfrac{^-4}{20}$ and $\dfrac{4}{^-20}$

5. Perform each of the following computations. Leave your answers in simplest form.

_____ (a) $\dfrac{2}{3} + \dfrac{4}{5}$

_____ (b) $\dfrac{3}{4} - \dfrac{2}{3}$

_____ (c) $\dfrac{5}{3} \cdot \dfrac{27}{40}$

_____ (d) $\left(3\dfrac{1}{4} + 7\dfrac{1}{8}\right) \div 8\dfrac{1}{2}$

6. Find the additive and multiplicative inverses for each of the following.

_____ _____ (a)   8

_____ _____ (b) $3\dfrac{1}{2}$

_____ _____ (c) $\dfrac{^-1}{4}$

_____ _____ (d) $\dfrac{3}{8}$

7. The ratio of boys to girls in Mr. Joiner's class is 5 to 7. If there are 15 boys in the class, how many total students are in the class?

8. Sunflower seeds are packed in packages each weighing $3\frac{1}{4}$ ounces. If there is a supply of $15\frac{1}{2}$ pounds of sunflower seeds, how many packages of seeds can be packed? How many ounces of sunflower seeds will be left over? (16 oz. = 1 pound)

9. Estimate each of the following, indicating if the actual answer is greater than or less than the estimate.

   (a) $\dfrac{199}{198} + \dfrac{35}{17}$

   (b) $4\dfrac{10}{11} + 3\dfrac{8}{9} + \dfrac{13}{14} + \dfrac{1}{20}$

   (c) $5\dfrac{19}{20} - 2\dfrac{9}{10} + 1\dfrac{1}{100}$

10. Estimate by rounding the fractions.

   _____ (a) $7\dfrac{8}{9} \cdot 5\dfrac{1}{13}$

   _____ (b) $\dfrac{34\frac{9}{10}}{4\frac{9}{10}}$

   _____ (c) $\dfrac{14\frac{19}{39}}{\frac{19}{39}}$

11. A plumber needs four sections of pipe $2\frac{7}{8}$ feet long. Can this be cut from a 12 foot section? If so, how much pipe will be left over? If not, why not?

12. Heidi's class had 17 A's out of 30 students and Barbara's class had 15 A's out of 27 students. Which class had the higher ratio of A's? Why?

13. Mabel read 20 pages of a book in 15 minutes. If she continues to read at the same rate, how many pages will she read in 25 minutes?

14. Solve the following for x.

_____ (a) $2x - 3 = 14$

_____ (b) $\frac{2}{3}x - 3 = 14 - x$

_____ (c) $3^x = 729$

_____ (d) $3^{-x} = \frac{1}{729}$

15. Write a story that requires the division $1\frac{3}{4} \div \frac{1}{2}$.

    _____

16. Find a rational number between 3/5 and 4/5.

    _____

17. Write a proportion that is a different form of the following:

    _____ $\dfrac{3}{4} = \dfrac{x}{2}$

18. Use properties of rational numbers to explain why $2 \div (3 \div 4) = (2 \div 3) \times 4$.

1. (a)

   (b)

2. $\frac{8}{10}, \frac{12}{15}, \frac{16}{20}$, and so on.

3. (a) $\frac{3}{4}$ (b) $\frac{c^2 y^4}{d}$ (c) $\frac{0}{1}$ (d) $\frac{1}{b}$

4. (a) $=$ (b) $<$ (c) $=$

5. (a) $\frac{22}{15}$ (b) $\frac{1}{12}$ (c) $\frac{9}{8}$ (d) $\frac{83}{68}$

6. (a) $^-8$ and $\frac{1}{8}$ (b) $^-3\frac{1}{2}$ and $\frac{2}{7}$ (c) $\frac{1}{4}$ and $\frac{^-4}{1}$

   (d) $\frac{^-3}{8}$ and $\frac{8}{3}$

7. 36

8. 76 packages, and $\frac{4}{13}$ oz. will be left over.

9. (a) more than 3   (b) Less than 10   (c) More than 4

10. (a) 40   (b) 7   (c) 29

11. Yes, 1/2 ft will be left.

12. Heidi's class because $\frac{17}{30} > \frac{15}{27}$.

13. $33\frac{1}{3}$ pages.

14. (a) $\frac{17}{2}$

    (b) $\frac{51}{5}$

    (c) 6

    (d) 6

15. Example: A rectangle with area 1 3/4 has width $\dfrac{1}{2}$. What is its length?

16. Example: $\dfrac{7}{10}$

17. There are several possible answers. One is $\dfrac{4}{3} = \dfrac{2}{x}$.

18.

$$2 \div (3 \div 4) = 2 \times \frac{1}{(3 \div 4)}; \text{ definition of division}$$

$$= 2 \times \frac{1}{3 \times \frac{1}{4}}; \text{ definition of division}$$

$$= 2 \times \frac{1}{\frac{3}{4}}; \text{ definition of multiplication}$$

$$= 2 \times \frac{4}{3}; \text{ multiplicative inverse}$$

$$= 2 \times \left(4 \times \frac{1}{3}\right); \text{ definition of division}$$

$$= 2 \times \left(\frac{1}{3} \times 4\right); \text{ commutative property of multiplication}$$

$$= \left(2 \times \frac{1}{3}\right) \times 4; \text{ associative property of multiplication}$$

$$= (2 \div 3) \times 4; \text{ definition of division}$$

Sample Assessment

1. For each of the following, draw a diagram illustrating the fraction.

    (a) $\dfrac{3}{4}$

    (b) $\dfrac{1}{5}$

2. Reduce each of the following rational numbers to simplest form.

    (a) $\dfrac{6^2}{48}$

    (b) $\dfrac{(xy)^2}{x^2 y^2}$

    (c) $\dfrac{3x+9x^2}{x+3x^2}$

3. Perform each of the following computations.

    (a) $\dfrac{3}{8} + \dfrac{7}{12}$

    (b) $1 - \dfrac{1}{2} + \dfrac{1}{3} - \dfrac{1}{4} + \dfrac{1}{5} - \dfrac{1}{6}$

    (c) $\left(5\dfrac{2}{7} + 2\dfrac{3}{7}\right) \div 2\dfrac{1}{2}$

    (d) $\dfrac{3}{2} - 4\dfrac{1}{3}$

4. Simplify each of the following. Write your answer in the form $\frac{a}{b}$, where a and b are integers and $\frac{a}{b}$ is in simplest form.

    (a) $$\dfrac{\dfrac{2}{3} - \dfrac{1}{6}}{\dfrac{2}{3} + \dfrac{1}{6}}$$

    (b) $$\dfrac{\dfrac{2}{9} \cdot \dfrac{3}{4}}{\left(\dfrac{2}{3}\right)^2}$$

5. Is the following statement true or false? (Justify your answer.) For all positive integers a, b such that $b \geq 2$, $\dfrac{a+1}{b-1} > \dfrac{a}{b}$.

6. A car travels 55 miles per hour and a plane travels 15 miles per minute. How far does the car travel when the plane travels 500 miles?

7. A $46\frac{5}{16}$ lb bag of nuts is packaged in $1\frac{3}{4}$ lb containers. The remaining nuts are given to the person packing the nuts. How much does the person get? Justify your answer.

8. If the ratio of boys to girls in a class is 3 to 8, will the ratios of boys to girls stay the same, become greater, or become lesser if 2 boys and 2 girls leave the class? Justify your answer?

9. Estimate each of the following, indicating if the actual answer is greater than or less than the estimate.

_____ (a) $\dfrac{29}{15} + \dfrac{198}{199}$

_____ (b) $5\dfrac{12}{13} + 2\dfrac{9}{10} + \dfrac{19}{20}$

_____ (c) $10\dfrac{4}{9} - 5\dfrac{1}{2} + \dfrac{99}{100}$

10. Estimate each of the following.

_____ (a) $7\dfrac{33}{100} \cdot 3$

_____ (b) $2\dfrac{25}{99} \cdot 8$

_____ (c) $\dfrac{4\dfrac{10}{99}}{\dfrac{1}{10}}$

11. Place $<$, $>$, or $=$ between each of the following pairs to make true statements.

_____ (a) $\dfrac{11}{23}$ and $\dfrac{33}{65}$

_____ (b) $\dfrac{7}{8}$ and $\dfrac{8}{9}$

_____ (c) $-\dfrac{6}{7}$ and $-\dfrac{11}{33}$

12. The ratio of oranges to apples in the gift basket is 3 to 5. If there are 9 oranges, how many apples are there?

13. If $9\frac{1}{8}$ lb of nails cost \$4.25, what is the cost of 292 lb?

14. The ratio of private school students to public school students in Adams City is 3 to 20. If there are 16,020 total students, how many are in private schools?

15. Solve the following for x.

_____ (a) $3x - 2 = 15$

_____ (b) $\frac{3}{2}x - 2 = 15 + x$

_____ (c) $2^{2x} = 64$

_____ (d) $2^{-x} = 64$

16. Write a story that requires the division: $1\frac{2}{3} \div \frac{1}{2}$.

17. _____ Find a rational number between $\frac{1}{8}$ and $\frac{2}{4}$.

18. _____ $\frac{2}{4} = \frac{7}{x}$. Write a proportion that is a different form of the following:

19. Use properties of rational numbers to explain why $3 \div (2 \div 5) = (3 \div 2) \times 5$

1. (a)

    (b)

2. (a) $\dfrac{3}{4}$ (b) 1   (c) 3

3. (a) $\dfrac{23}{24}$ (b) $\dfrac{37}{60}$ (c) $3\dfrac{3}{35}$ (d) $\dfrac{^-17}{6}$

4. (a) $\dfrac{3}{5}$ (b) $\dfrac{3}{8}$

5. True. When the denominator of a fraction (whose numerator and denominator are positive) decreases, the fraction increases. When the numerator increases the fraction increases as well. A more formal approach follows: $\dfrac{a+1}{b-1} > \dfrac{a}{b}$ if and only if $ab + b > ab$ $-a$ or $b > {}^-a$. The last inequality is true because $a > 0$ and $b \geq 2$.

6. $30\dfrac{5}{9}$ mi

7. A person gets approximately $\dfrac{13}{16}$ lb of nuts.

8. It will become smaller because $\dfrac{3x}{8x} > \dfrac{3x-2}{8x-2}$, since x is positive.

9. (a) less than 3   (b) less than 10   (c) less than 6

10. (a) 22   (b) 18   (c) 41

11. (a) <   (b) <   (c) <

12. 15 apples

13. $136

14. Approximately 2090 students

15. (a) $\dfrac{17}{3}$

(b) 34

(c) 3

(d) ⁻6

16. Answers will vary. For example, If the area of a rectangle is $1\dfrac{2}{3}$ and its width is $\dfrac{1}{2}$, what is its length?

17. One possibility is $\dfrac{3}{8}$.

18. Answers vary. For example, $\dfrac{4}{2} = \dfrac{x}{7}$.

19.

$$3 \div (2 \div 5) = 3 \times \dfrac{1}{(2 \div 5)}; \text{ definition of division}$$

$$= 3 \times \dfrac{1}{2 \times \dfrac{1}{5}}; \text{ definition of division}$$

$$= 3 \times \dfrac{1}{\dfrac{2}{5}}; \text{ definition of multiplication}$$

$$= 3 \times \dfrac{5}{2}; \text{ multiplicative inverse}$$

$$= 3 \times \left(5 \times \dfrac{1}{2}\right); \text{ definition of division}$$

$$= 3 \times \left(\dfrac{1}{2} \times 5\right); \text{ commutative property of multiplication}$$

$$= \left(3 \times \dfrac{1}{2}\right) \times 5; \text{ associative property of multiplication}$$

$$= (3 \div 2) \times 5; \text{ definition of division}$$

Sample Assessment

1. Place >, <, or = in the space between each of the following pairs to make true statements.

    (a) $2.\overline{23}$ _____ $\sqrt{5}$ (b) $0.\overline{3}$ _____ 1/3

    (c) $0.\overline{4} + 0.\overline{5}$ _____ 1   (d) $3.\overline{78}$ _____ $3.7\overline{8}$

2. For which values of k can $\dfrac{k}{3840}$ be written as a terminating decimal. Explain your reasoning.

3. Use fractions to justify the algorithm for the subtraction in the following.

    $8.07 - 2.3$

4. Round each of the following numbers as specified.

    (a)   508.576 to the nearest hundredth _____
    (b)   508.576 to the nearest tenth   _____
    (c)   508.576 to the nearest hundred   _____

5. Convert each of the following rational numbers to the form $\dfrac{a}{b}$, where a and b are integers and $b \neq 0$.

    (a)   0.27 _____   (b) 3.104 _____   (c) $0.2\overline{4}$ _____   (d) 0.24 _____

6. Convert each of the following fractions to decimals that either terminate or repeat.

    (a)   3/40 _____   (b)   2/13 _____

7. Find an approximation for $\sqrt{15}$ rounded to the nearest thousandth.

    _____

8. Write each of the following in scientific notation.

   (a) 5,268,000 _____   (b) 0.000325 _____

9. Classify each of the following as a rational or irrational number.

   (a) 6.76776777677776... _____

   (b) $\dfrac{1}{\sqrt{15}}$ _____

   (c) $\dfrac{\sqrt{32}}{\sqrt{2}}$ _____

10. Without using a calculator, simplify each of the following if possible:

    (a) $16^{-\frac{1}{4}}$ _____   (b) $64^{-\frac{1}{6}}$ _____

11. Solve each of the following for x, where x is a real number.

    (a) $x\sqrt{3} - 2 = 5x\sqrt{3}$ _____   (b) $0.\overline{9} - x = 1$ _____

    (c) $0.\overline{4} + x = 1$ _____   (d) $5.2x - 0.01 < 0.2x + 3.6$ _____

12. Use mental mathematics to find the following and explain your approach.

    (a) What percent of 10,000 is 900?

    (b) 60% of 2,000.

13. Wheel's Bicycle shop advertised a bicycle for 15% off for a savings of $36. The bicycle did not sell so it was offered at a 20% discount off the sale price.

    (a)   What did the bicycle sell for regularly? _____

    (b)   What is the amount of the current discount? _____

14. Write each of the following as a percent.

    (a)   0.1 _____   (b) $\dfrac{1}{6}$ _____

    (c)   1 _____   (d) $3\dfrac{3}{8}$ _____

15. Two automobile dealers, A and B, had the same car which was listed at $18,000. Dealer A offered a $1,200 rebate and would negotiate a further 8% discount after rebate. Dealer B offered an 8% discount and would negotiate a further $1,200 rebate.

    (a)   Which dealer has the lowest price? _____

    (b)   What is the lowest price? _____

16. Barbara correctly answered 85% of the questions on his 200-question biology final. Fernando scored a 90% on his 180-question chemistry final.

    (a)   Who answered more questions correctly? _____

    (b)   Who answered more questions incorrectly? _____

*17. If Misha receives $4\dfrac{1}{2}$% interest compounded daily on her investment, then what is her effective annual yield in a non-leap year? _____

*18. The Cha family has decided that they need to invest some money for their daughter's college expenses. They estimate that they will need $80,000 in 16 years. If they can find an account that pays 11% interest compounded weekly, how much do they need to invest? _____

1. (a) $<$ (b) $=$ (c) $=$ (d) $<$

2. Because $3840 = 2^8 \cdot 3 \cdot 5$ the prime factorization of the denominator of this fraction will contain only powers of 2 and 5 if and only if k is a multiple of 3.

3. $8.07 - 2.3 = \dfrac{807}{100} - \dfrac{23}{10}$

$= \dfrac{807}{100} - \dfrac{230}{100}$

$= \dfrac{807 - 230}{100}$

$= \dfrac{577}{100}$

$= 5.77$

4. (a) 508.58   (b) 508.6   (c) 500

5. (a) $\dfrac{27}{100}$ (b) $\dfrac{3104}{1000}$ or $\dfrac{388}{125}$ (c) $\dfrac{22}{90}$ or $\dfrac{11}{45}$ (d) $\dfrac{24}{100}$ or $\dfrac{6}{25}$

6. (a) 0.075   (b) $0.\overline{153846}$

7. 3.873

8. (a) $5.268 \cdot 10^6$ (b) $3.25 \cdot 10^{-4}$

9. (a) Irrational, if pattern continues
    (b) Irrational
    (c) Rational

10. (a) 1/2   (b) 1/2

11. (a) $\dfrac{^-1}{2\sqrt{3}}$ or $\dfrac{^-\sqrt{3}}{6}$ (b) 0

     (c) $\dfrac{5}{9}$ or $0.\overline{5}$ (d) $x < 0.722$

12. (a) 9%, answers vary for the approach, for example, 900/10,000 reduces to 9/100 or 0.09 which is 9%.
    (b) 1,200, answers vary for the approach, for example, 10% of 2,000 is 200 so 60% is $6 \cdot 200 = 1200$.

13. (a) $240   (b) $40.80

14. (a)   10%   (b) $16.\overline{6}\%$ or $16\frac{2}{3}\%$ (c)   100%   (d)   337.5%

15. (a)   Dealer B (b) $15,360

16. (a)   Barbara   (b)   Barbara

17. 4.602%

18. $13,789.20

Sample Assessment

1. Place >, <, or = in the space between each of the following pairs to make true statements.

    (a) $1.\overline{73}$ _____ $\sqrt{3}$

    (b) $0.\overline{5}$ _____ 1/2

    (c) $1 - 0.\overline{5}$ _____ $0.\overline{4}$

    (d) $2.\overline{54}$ _____ $2.5\overline{4}$

2. For which values of k can $k/240$ be written as a terminating decimal. Explain your reasoning.

3. Use fractions to justify the algorithm for the subtraction in the following.

    $23.6 - 8.34$

4. Round each of the following numbers as specified.

    (a) 245.567 to the nearest hundredth _____
    (b) 245.567 to the nearest unit _____
    (c) 245.567 to the nearest hundred _____

5. Convert each of the following rational numbers to the form $\frac{a}{b}$, where a and b are integers and $b \neq 0$.

    (a) 0.38 _____

    (b) 2.607 _____

    (c) $0.4\overline{7}$ _____

    (d) $0.\overline{324}$ _____

6. Convert each of the following fractions to decimals that either terminate or repeat.

    (a) 6/30 _____

    (b) 5/11 _____

7. Find an approximation for $\sqrt{11}$ rounded to the nearest thousandth. _____

8.   Write each of the following in scientific notation.

   (a)   3286 _____   (b)   0.0000032 _____

9.   Classify each of the following as a rational or irrational number.

   (a) $\sqrt{2} + 8$ _____   (b) $\dfrac{7}{22}$ _____

   (c)   3.14114111411114. . . _____

10.   Without a calculator, simplify each of the following if possible.

   (a) $2^{1/2} \cdot 2^{1/2}$ _____   (b) $32^{1/5}$ _____

11.   Solve each of the following for x, if possible, where x is a real number.

   (a) $5x\sqrt{2} - x\sqrt{2} = 7x\sqrt{2} + 5$ _____   (b) $\dfrac{x}{0.4} + 80 = 0.5 + 0.8$ _____

   (c) $0.\overline{3} + x = 0.\overline{7}$ _____   (d) $1.\overline{9} - x = 2$ _____

12.   Use mental mathematics to find the following and explain your reasoning.

   (a)   40% of 50.

   (b)   What percent of 500 is 40?

13. A sale at Carney's Electronics offers a specific model of Sony radio at 20% off the regular price. If the sale price of the radios is $45, what is the regular price? _____

14. Write each of the following as a percent:

(a) $\frac{1}{5}$ _____   (b) $\frac{1}{100}$ _____   (c) 3.042 _____   (d) $0.\overline{6}$ _____

15. Kelly counted 277 distinct beluga whales in the St. Lawrence Seaway in one week. The following week she counted 343 distinct belugas. What was the percent (to two decimal places of accuracy) of increase in the whales counted? _____

16. Write each of the following as decimals.

(a) $\frac{1}{4}$% _____   (b) 167 % _____   (c) 100% _____

*17. Maan invests $4,500 with First National Bank at $5\frac{1}{4}$% simple interest.

(a) How much interest does Maan earn after one year? _____

(b) How much money did Maan have at the end of the year? _____

(c) If Maan reinvested everything for a second year, how much money would he have at the end of the second year? _____

*18. Sheila invests $3,200 at 7% interest compounded quarterly.

(a) How much does she have after 10 years? _____

(b) 20 years? _____

(c) 50 years? _____

1. (a) $>$ (b) $>$ (c) $=$ (d) $>$

2. Because $240 = 2^4 \cdot 3 \cdot 5$, the prime factorization of the denominator of this fraction will contain only powers of 2 and 5 if and only if k is a factor of 3.

3. $23.6 - 8.34 = 23.60 - 8.34$
$$= \frac{2360}{100} - \frac{834}{100}$$
$$= \frac{1526}{100}$$
$$= 15.26$$

4. (a) 245.57   (b) 246   (c) 200

5. (a) 38/100 or 19/50   (b) 2607/1000   (c) 43/90   (d) 324/999 or 36/111

6. (a) 0.2   (b) $0.\overline{45}$

7. 3,317

8. (a) $3.286 \cdot 10^3$ (b) $3.2 \cdot 10^{-6}$

9. (a) Irrational
   (b) Rational
   (c) Irrational, if pattern continues.

10. (a) 2   (b) 2

11. (a) $\dfrac{^-5}{3\sqrt{2}}$ or $\dfrac{^-5\sqrt{2}}{6}$ (b) -31.48

   (c) $0.\overline{4}$ or $\dfrac{4}{9}$ (d) 0

12. (a) 20, reasoning varies, for example, 10% of 50 is 5 so 40% of 50 is $4 \cdot 5 = 20$.

   (b) 8%, reasoning varies, for example, $40/500 = 4/50 = 8/100 = 8\%$.

13. $56.25

14. (a) 20%   (b) 1%   (c) 304.2%   (d) 66 2/3% or $66.\overline{6}\%$

15. 23.83%

16. (a) 0.0025   (b) 1.67   (c) 1

17. (a) $236.25   (b) $4736.25   (c) $4984.90

18. (a) $6405.11   (b) 12,820.45   (c) 102,809.57

Sample Assessment

1. A fair coin was flipped three times and landed heads three times. What is the probability of a head on the next toss? _____

2. A bag contains five red candies, six white candies, and seven blue candies. Suppose one piece of candy is drawn at random. Find the probability for each of the following

   (a) A white candy is drawn. _____

   (b) A red or blue candy is drawn. _____

   (c) Neither a white nor a blue candy is drawn. _____

3. A box contains three blue cards and three white cards. If two cards are drawn one at a time, find the probability that both cards are blue if the draws are made as follows:

   (a) With replacement _____

   (b) Without replacement _____

4. In a NASA rocket firing, the probability of the success of the first stage is 95%, of the second stage 97%, and of the third stage 98%. What is the probability for success for the three-stage rocket? _____

5. (a) If a letter is drawn from container 1, shown below, and placed in container 2, and then a letter is drawn from container 2, what is the probability that the letter is a *T*? _____

MATH	*HAT*
#1	#2

   (b) If a container above is selected at random, and then a letter is selected at random from the chosen container, what is the probability that the letter is a *T*? _____

6. If two dice are rolled 360 times, approximately how many times should you expect the sums of 2, 3, or 12? _____

7. A teacher has prepared a 5-item test with the first three items being true or false and the last two items being multiple choice with four choices each. What is the probability that a student will score 100 percent if every answer is chosen at random? _____

8. A committee of three is selected at random from a set consisting of five Democrats, eight Republicans, and two Independents. _____

   (a)   What is the probability that the committee consists of all Democrats? _____

   (b)   What is the probability that the committee consists of no Republicans? _____

9. There were seven nominees for president and four nominees for vice president. In how many ways can the slate be chosen? _____

10. Compute $\dfrac{100!}{99!}$. _____

11. How many different two-person committees can be formed from a group of six people?

   _____

12. If automobile license plates consist of two letters followed by four digits, how many different possible license plates are possible if letters and numbers can be repeated?

   _____

13. Given the spinner below, find each of the following.

(a) $P(A)$_____   (b) $P(B)$_____

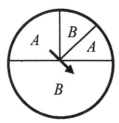

14. If the odds in favor of the Rangers winning the game are 7 to 5, what is the probability that they will win? _____

15. Two standard dice are rolled. What are the odds in favor of rolling a sum of 10?

_____

16. A sorority sold 132 tickets in a raffle for a $264 television set. What is the expected value of a single ticket if only one ticket wins? _____

17. How could picking three dates at random in the month of April be simulated using a random digit table? _____

1. $\dfrac{1}{2}$

2. (a) $\dfrac{6}{18}$ or $\dfrac{1}{3}$ (b) $\dfrac{12}{18}$ or $\dfrac{2}{3}$ (c) $\dfrac{5}{18}$

3. (a) $\dfrac{9}{36}$ or $\dfrac{1}{4}$ (b) $\dfrac{6}{30}$ or $\dfrac{1}{5}$

4. 0.90307 or approximately 0.9

5. (a) $\dfrac{5}{16}$ (b) $\dfrac{7}{24}$

6. 40

7. $\dfrac{1}{128}$

8. (a) $\dfrac{60}{2730}$ or $\dfrac{2}{91}$ (b) $\dfrac{210}{2330}$ or $\dfrac{1}{13}$

9. 28 ways

10. 100

11. 15

12. 6,760,000

13. (a) $P(A) = \dfrac{3}{8}$ (b) $P(B) = \dfrac{5}{8}$

14. $\dfrac{7}{12}$

15. $\dfrac{3}{33}$ or $\dfrac{1}{11}$

16. $2.00

17. Answers vary, for example, let the numbers 01, 02, 03, 04, 05, . . . , 29, 30 represent the dates of the month. Pick a starting place and mark off blocks of two until three of the blocks are obtained.

Sample Assessment

1. What is the probability of a fair coin landing heads four times in a row?

2. A box contains four red marbles, seven white marbles, and five blue marbles. If one piece marble is drawn at random, find the probability for each of the following.

    (a)   A blue marble is drawn. _____

    (b)   A red or a blue marble is drawn. _____

    (c)   Neither a red nor a blue marble is drawn. _____

3. A box contains four red marbles, seven white marbles, and five blue marbles. If two marbles are drawn one at a time, find the probability that both marbles are white if the draws are made as follows:

    (a)   With replacement _____   (b) Without replacement _____

4. The probability of Ann passing her math test is 90%. The probability she passes her English test is 80%. The probability she passes her Chemistry test is 70%. What is the probability she passes all three tests? _____

5. (a)   If a letter is drawn from container 1, shown below, and placed in container number 2, then a letter is drawn from container 2, what is the probability that the letter is a *O*?

    _____

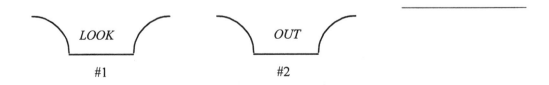

#1   #2

    (b)   If a letter is drawn from container number 1 above and then a letter is drawn from container number 2, what is the probability of the outcome *OO*? _____

6. If two dice are rolled 360 times, approximately how many times should you expect a sum of 7? _____

7. A teacher has prepared a six-item test with the first three items being true or false and the last three items being multiple choice with four choices each. What is the probability that a student will score 0 if every answer is chosen at random? _____

8. A committee of two is selected at random from a set consisting of three Democrats, four Republicans, and one Independent.

    (a)   What is the probability that the committee consists of no Republicans? _____

    (b)   What is the probability that the committee consists of all Republicans? _____

9. There were eight nominees for president and three nominees for vice president. In how many ways can the slate be chosen? _____

10. Compute $\dfrac{200!}{198!}$ _____

11. How many different four-person committees can be formed from a group of six people?

    _____

12. If automobile license plates consist of three letters followed by three digits, how many different possible license plates are possible if letters and numbers can be repeated?

    _____

13. Given the spinner below, find each of the following.

    (a) $P(A)$ _____

    (b) $P(B)$ _____

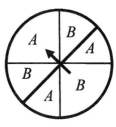

14. If the odds in favor of the Tigers winning their next game are 8 to 4, what is the probability that they will win? _____

15. Two standard dice are rolled. What are the odds in favor of rolling a sum of 8?

    _____

16. Joe's baseball team sold 200 chances to win a $250 set of golf clubs. What is the expected value of a single chance if only one chance wins? _____

17. How could picking three letters of the alphabet at random be simulated using a random digit table?

1. $\dfrac{1}{16}$

2. (a) $\dfrac{5}{16}$ (b) $\dfrac{9}{16}$ (c) $\dfrac{7}{16}$

3. (a) $\dfrac{49}{256}$ (b) $\dfrac{42}{240}$ or $\dfrac{7}{40}$

4. 0.504

5. (a) $\dfrac{6}{16}$ or $\dfrac{3}{8}$ (b) $\dfrac{1}{6}$

6. 60

7. $\dfrac{57}{512}$

8. (a) $\dfrac{12}{56}$ or $\dfrac{3}{14}$ (b) $\dfrac{12}{56}$ or $\dfrac{3}{14}$

9. 24 ways

10. 39,800

11. 15

12. $26^3 \cdot 10^3$ or 17,576,000

13. (a) $P(A) = \dfrac{1}{2}$ (b) $P(B) = \dfrac{1}{2}$

14. $\dfrac{4}{12}$ or $\dfrac{1}{3}$

15. 5 to 31

16. $1.25

17. Answers may vary, for example, mark off the digits in blocks of two. Let the numbers 01, 02, 03, 04, 05, . . . 25, 26 represent the consecutive letters of the alphabet. Disregard blocks of two not in this range.

Sample Assessment

1. Claude paid $38.80 for dinner for himself and two friends. If one friend's meal cost twice as much as Claude's and Claude's meal cost the same as his other friend, answer the following:

   (a) What is the mean cost of the meals?   _____

   (b) What is the median cost of the meals?   _____

   (c) What is the mode cost of the meals?   _____

2. For the scores 98   98   98   98   45   84   84   52   45   37, find the following.

   (a)   mean   _____

   (b)   median   _____

   (c)   mode   _____

   (d)   range   _____

   (e)   standard deviation _____

3. The budget for the Women's Center is $1,000,000. If $500,000 is spent on advertising, $150,000 is spent on conferences, and the remainder is spent on long-term securities, draw a circle graph to indicate how the money is spent. Include percents on the graph.

4. If the median is greater than the mean on a set of test scores, describe the distribution.

5. Twenty test scores are given below.

31	30	23	27	19
26	28	38	17	29
26	34	21	32	32
22	12	26	39	25

(a) Make a grouped frequency table for these scores, using 10 to start the first class and having interval size 5.

(b) Draw a histogram for the grouped data.

(c) Draw an ordered stem-and-leaf plot for the data.

(d) Construct a box plot for the data.

6. Explain how to determine if a score is an outlier when constructing a box plot.

7. (a) The mean age of members of a class reunion was 71.9. The next year the mean age was 71.5 years. How can the mean age decrease when all the class members are a year older?

    (b) The mean age of 10 persons in a room is 15 years. A 50-year-old person walks in. How much is the mean increased? _____

8. If all the students in the class scored 100 on an exam, what is the standard deviation? Tell why you answered the way that you did. _____

9. An advertisement claims "Four out of five doctors surveyed recommend Tryit for their patients with arthritis." Discuss why you would or would not accept this as a valid claim to product superiority.

1. (a) Approximately $12.93
   (b) $9.70
   (c) $9.70

2. (a) Mean, 73.9;
   (b) Median, 84;
   (c) Mode, 98;
   (d) Range, 61
   (e) Approximately 24.57

3.

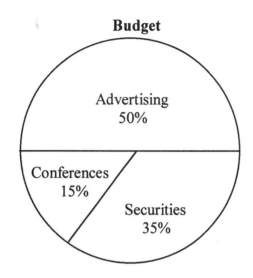

Budget

Advertising 50%

Conferences 15%

Securities 35%

4. There are more high scores than low ones, but the low ones lower the mean.

5. (a)

Class	Frequency
10-14	1
15-19	2
20-24	3
25-29	7
30-34	5
35-39	2
Total	20

5. (cont.)

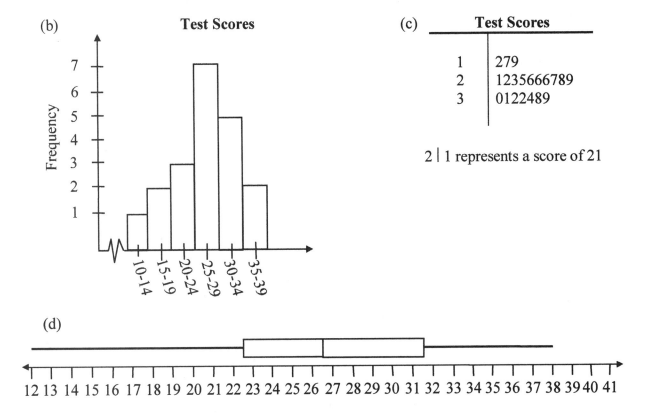

(b) **Test Scores**

(c)

	Test Scores
1	279
2	1235666789
3	0122489

2 | 1 represents a score of 21

(d)

6. The outlier is any score that is more than 1.5 IQR above the upper quartile or more than 1.5 IQR below the lower quartile.

7. (a) Answers vary, for example, more of the older members have died or did not attend or a greater number of younger members attended.

   (a) Approximately 3.18 years.

8. The standard deviation is 0. The mean for this group of scores is 100 and so the differences between the mean and the scores in this case are all 0. Summing the differences, dividing by the number of scores and finding the square root results in 0. There is no variation in the scores and the standard deviation tells how dispersed the scores are. Since they are all the same there is no dispersion and so the variation and the standard deviation are 0.

9. You do not know who was surveyed, how many were surveyed, or what types of questions were asked. The claim should not be taken at face value without more information.

Sample Assessment

1. The weights in pounds of six elementary students are: 80, 92, 71, 63, 76, and 83. Find the following.

   (a)   mean   _____

   (b)   median   _____

   (c)   mode   _____

   (d)   range   _____

   (e)   standard deviation to the nearest tenth of a pound.   _____

2. The mean average for Joyce's 11 test scores was 62.5. How much will a score of 100 change her mean average? _____

3. What happens to mean and the standard deviation of a set of scores if each score is increased by 5? Explain.

4. Professor Abel corrected 20 papers and found the mean to be 70. He then corrected 30 more papers and found the mean for this group to be 80. What is the mean of the combined group of 50 students.   _____

5. The weights in pounds for offensive linemen on the pro football team are 276, 284, 275, 276, 282, 280, 279, 273, 275, 270, 272, construct a line plot for the data.

6. The following are the weights in pounds of 30 students at the Summer Math Camp.

146	163	142	147	135	153	140	135	128	145
146	158	140	147	136	148	152	144	156	150
168	126	138	176	163	119	154	165	142	135

(a)   Construct a frequency table for the data above with the first class starting at 115 and interval size 10.

(b)   Draw a histogram depicting the data.

7. The quiz scores for Mr. Read's and Miss Sol's classes are given below.

Mr. Read	Miss Sol
72	90
78	88
85	78
92	83
75	96
76	92
89	90
96	84
78	75
92	98
90	93
80	92

(a) Draw a back-to-back stem and leaf plot for the two classes.

(b) Give the interquartile range for each set of scores. _____

(c) Are there any outliers for either set of data? If yes, what are they? _____

(d) Draw box plots to compare the two sets of data.

(e) What can you say about the two sets of data?

1. (a) 77.5   (b) 78   (c) no mode   (d) 29   (e) Approximately 9.14

2. 3.125

3. The mean is increased by 5. The standard deviation stays the same.

4. 76

5.
Weights for Offensive Linemen

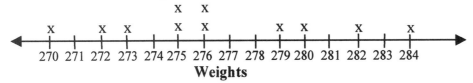

6. (a)

Class of Weights	Frequency
115-124	1
125-134	2
135-144	10
145-154	10
155-164	4
165-174	2
175-184	1
Total	30

(b)   **Student Weights at Summer Math Camp**

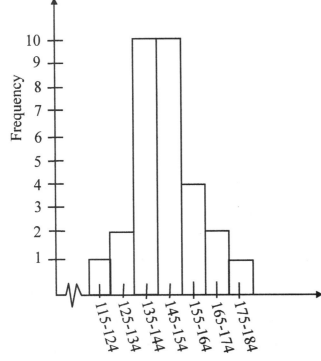

Class Weight (in Pounds)

7. (a)   **TEST SCORES**

Miss Sol's Class		Mr. Read's Class
85	7	25688
843	8	059
86332200	9	0226

$9 \mid 8 = 98$

(b) The IQR for Mr. Read is 14. The IQR for Miss Sol is 9.

(c) There are no outliers for either set of data.

(d)   **TEST SCORES**

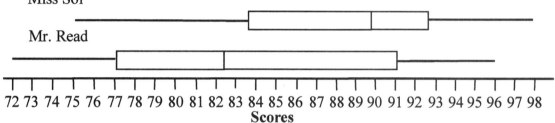

(e)   Miss Sol's class did better on the quiz than Mr. Read's class. 75% of Miss Sol's class scored above the median for Mr. Read's class.

Sample Assessment

1. If six lines are in a single plane, explain whether or not they can determine an octagon.

2. Are the angles of a triangle considered to be supplementary? _____
   Explain your answer.

3. What is the least number of edges that a polyhedron may have? _____
   Sketch an example.

4. Explain whether a soccer ball is a polyhedron.

5. Classify the following as true or false. If false, tell why.

   _____(a)   Two distinct lines that do not intersect are parallel.

   _____(b)   No square is a rectangle.

   _____(c)   If a plane contains one point of a line, then it must contain the entire line.

   _____(d)   For any two distinct points A and B, $\overrightarrow{AB} = \overleftarrow{BA}$.

   _____(e)   A ray contains no endpoints.

6. Describe each of the following sets of points with reference to the given figure.

_____ (a) (plane *AFD*) ∩ (plane *XYE*)

_____ (b) (Plane *XYE*) ∩ $\overrightarrow{AE}$

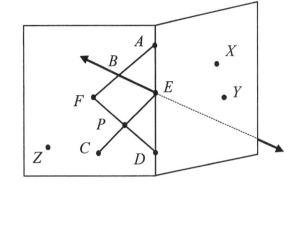

_____ (c) $\overline{BE} \cap \overline{CE}$

_____ (d) $\overline{CE} \cap \triangle ADF$

_____ (e) $\overleftrightarrow{AE} \cap \overleftrightarrow{DE}$

_____ (f) $\overrightarrow{EB} \cap \overrightarrow{EC}$

_____ (g) (interior $\triangle ADF$) ∩ $\overrightarrow{DE}$

7. If the measure of an angle is 23°17′18″, what is the measure of its supplement? _____

8. If the non-base angle of an isosceles triangle has a measure of 70°, what is the measure of each base angle? _____

9. How many diagonals does a decagon have? _____

10. If $9x°$ and $(5x + 62)°$ are the measures of complementary angles, what is the measure of each angle? _____

11. Is a rhombus a regular polygon? Explain your answer.

12. Given the figure shown with $\overrightarrow{AX} \parallel \overrightarrow{DY}$, find the following:

_____(a)   m(∠1)
_____(b)   m(∠2)
_____(c)   m(∠3)
_____(d)   m(∠4)
_____(e)   m(∠5)

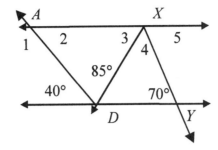

13. In the figure, how is the measure of angle 4 related to the sum of the measures of angle 1 and angle 2? _____
Justify your answer.

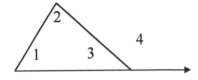

14. Draw each of the following.

(a)   A simple closed curve that is not a polygon.

(b)   A convex quadrilateral.

15. Sketch a polyhedron that has 9 faces. Show all unseen edges by dotting them.

*16. Which of the figures are traversable? For those that are traversable, circle all possible starting points.

(a)   (b)

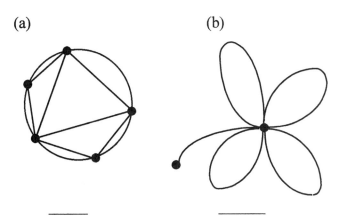

_____   _____

(c)

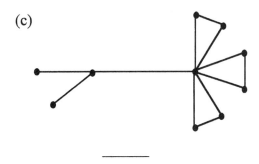

_____

1. Six lines cannot determine an octagon. The octagon has eight sides, at most two of which could be collinear.

2. The angles of a triangle do sum to 180°, but the angles are not supplementary. Supplementary angles are in pairs, while a triangle has three angles.

3. Six edges are the minimum. The drawings may vary.

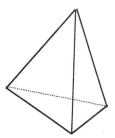

4. A soccer ball is not a polyhedron. A polyhedron has faces that lie in a plane. A soccer ball's faces do not.

5. (a) False; they could be skew.
    (b) False; all squares are rectangles.
    (c) False; the line can pass through the plane and intersect it in one point.
    (d) False; the rays lie on the same line but only overlap in a segment. They are not the same ray.
    (e) False, it has one end point.

6. (a) $\overleftrightarrow{AD}$
    (b) $\overrightarrow{AE}$
    (c) Point E
    (d) Points P and E
    (e) $\overrightarrow{AE}$
    (f) Point E
    (g) $\varnothing$

7. 156° 42′ 42″

8. 55°

9. 35

10. 18° and 72°

11. No, to be a regular polygon all sides and all angles must be congruent. The angles of a rhombus are not necessarily congruent.

12. (a) 140°   (b) 40°   (c) 55°
    (d) 55°   (e) 70°

13. The measure of angle 4 is equal to the sum of the measures of angles 1 and 2. A justification follows.

    $m(\angle 3) + m(\angle 4) = 180°$
    $m(\angle 1) + m(\angle 2) + m(\angle 3) = 180°$
    Therefore $m(\angle 3) + m(\angle 4) = m(\angle 1) + m(\angle 2) + m(\angle 3)$ which implies
    $m(\angle 4) = m(\angle 1) + m(\angle 2)$.

14. Answers may vary. For example,
    (a)
    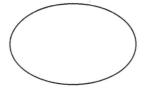

    (b)

15. Answers may vary. For example,
    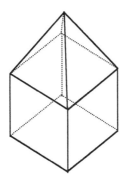

16. (a) Traversable

(b)

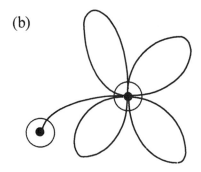

(c)   Not traversable

Sample Assessment

1. Sketch two angles whose intersection is exactly three points.

2. Sketch and name two angles that have a common vertex and a common side, but are not adjacent angles. _____

3. What is the number of vertices in an octagonal prism? _____

4. If planes α and β are distinct planes having points X, Y, and Z in common, what conclusion can you make about points X, Y, and Z?

   Why?

5. Classify the following as true or false. If false, tell why.

   _____(a) For any line $\overleftrightarrow{AB}$ and point C such that $C \in \overleftrightarrow{AB}$, there is one and only one plane containing both C and $\overleftrightarrow{AB}$.

   _____ (b) A parallelogram has four acute angles.

   _____ (c) A line segment contains an infinite number of points.

   _____ (d) The union of two rays is always a line.

_____ (e) For any two distinct points A and B, $\overrightarrow{AB} = \overrightarrow{BA}$.

_____ (f) If $\overrightarrow{AB} = \overrightarrow{CA}$, then A must be a different name for C.

_____ (g) Every equilateral triangle is a scalene triangle.

6. Describe each of the following sets of points with reference to the given figure.

_____(a) $\alpha \cap \beta$

_____ (b) $\triangle ADF \cap \overrightarrow{BE}$

_____ (c) $\overrightarrow{AF} \cap \overline{BE}$

_____ (d) $\angle CAF \cap \overrightarrow{CF}$

_____ (e) $\overline{AE} \cup \overleftrightarrow{FE}$

_____ (f) $\overrightarrow{BD} \cup \overrightarrow{BA}$

_____ (g)   (interior $\triangle ADF$) $\cap \overleftrightarrow{AF}$

_____ (h) $\overline{AE} \cup \overline{EF}$

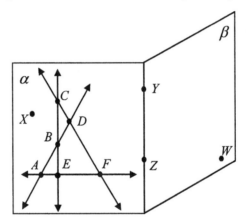

7. What is the measure of each angle in a regular dodecagon? _____

8. Find a pattern to describe the number of diagonals in a polygon. Describe the method used
    to find the pattern.

9. A rectangle has been defined as a parallelogram in which one of the angles is a right angle. Explain why a rectangle must have four right angles.

10. If $5x°$ and $(7x - 12)°$ are the measures for vertical angles formed by two intersecting lines, what is the measure of each angle?_____

11. (a) Find 28° 29′ 46″ − 16° 48′ 59″. _____

    (b) Express 5.4° in terms of degrees, minutes, and seconds. _____

12. Given the figure shown with $\overleftrightarrow{AX} \parallel \overleftrightarrow{DY}$, find the following:

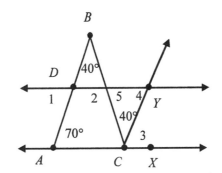

____(a) m(∠1)

____(b) m(∠2)

____(c) m(∠3)

____(d) m(∠4)

____(e) m(∠5)

13. If $\overrightarrow{AX}$ bisects ∠DAB and $\overrightarrow{AY}$ bisects ∠BAC, show $\overrightarrow{AX} \perp \overrightarrow{AY}$.

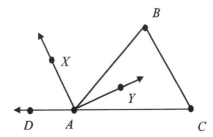

14. Draw each of the following curves.

(a)   A closed curve that is not simple.

(b)   A concave hexagon.

15. Explain whether or not the following could fold into a cube.

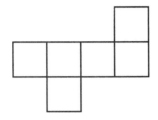

16. Sketch a three-dimensional drawing of a brick.

17. Explain whether or not a cone has to have a circular base.

*18. Which of the figures are traversable? For those that are traversable, circle all possible starting points.

(a)   (b)   (c)

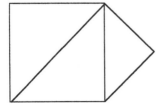   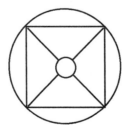   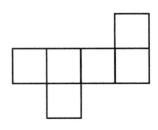

_____   _____   _____

1. $\angle ABC \cap \angle CAD = \{A, D, C\}$

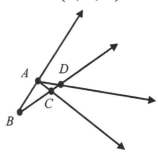

2. $\angle ABC$ and $\angle DBC$

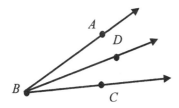

3. 16

4. X, Y, and Z are collinear because if two distinct planes intersect, they intersect in a line.

5. (a) False, there are an infinite number of planes containing the line.
    (b) False, the sum of the four interior angles in a parallelogram must be 360°. With four acute angles this cannot happen.
    (c) True
    (d) False, for example in the figure below, $\overrightarrow{AB} \cup \overrightarrow{CD}$ is not a line.

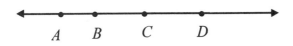

    (e) False, one ray starts at A and goes in the B direction and one ray starts at B and goes in the A direction.
    (f) True.
    (g) False, in an equilateral triangle at least 2 sides are congruent.

6. (a) $\overrightarrow{YZ}$ (b) Points B and E (c) Point E
    (d) Points C and F (e) $\overline{FE}$ (f) $\overleftrightarrow{AB}$
    (g) $\varnothing$ (h) $\overline{AF}$

7. 150°

8. The pattern can be determined by examining simpler cases and building a pattern. The formula is $\dfrac{n(n-3)}{2}$.

9. Let *ABCD* be the rectangle shown, with ∠*A* as a right angle.

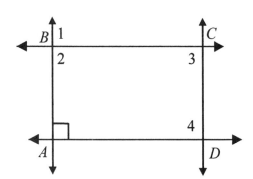

Because rectangle *ABCD* is a parallelogram, $\overleftrightarrow{BC} \parallel \overleftrightarrow{AD}$ and $\overleftrightarrow{AB} \parallel \overleftrightarrow{CD}$. Corresponding angles, ∠*BAD* and ∠1 are congruent, and thus ∠1 is a right angle. Because ∠1 and ∠2 are supplementary, ∠2 is a right angle. Similarly, it can be proved that ∠3 and ∠4 are right angles.

10. 30°

11. (a)   11° 40′ 47″
     (b)   5° 24′ 0″

12. (a)   70°   (b)   110°   (c)   70°
     (d)   70°   (e)   70°

13. $\overrightarrow{AX}$ bisects ∠*DAB*, so ∠*DAX* ≅ ∠*XAB*. $\overrightarrow{AY}$ bisects ∠*BAC*, so ∠*BAY* ≅ ∠*YAC*.
     m(∠*DAX*) + m(∠*XAB*) + m(∠*BAY*) + m(∠*YAC*) = 180°
     Hence, 2m(∠*XAB*) + 2m(∠*BAY*) = 180° and m(∠*XAB*) + m(∠*BAY*) = 90°

     Therefore, ∠*XAY* is a right angle. Hence $\overrightarrow{AX} \perp \overrightarrow{AY}$.

14. (a)   For example,   (b)

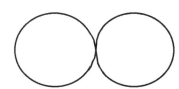   

15.   It could form a cube. There are six squares that could fold to make the faces of a cube.

16. Answers may vary. For example,

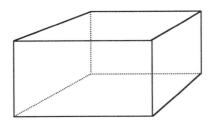

17. A cone does not have to have a circular base. Any simple closed shape is acceptable for the base of a cone.

18. (a)   Traversable

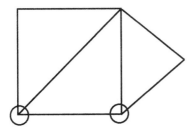

    (b)   Not traversable
    (c)   Not traversable

Sample Assessment

1. Given the figures, state whether the triangles are congruent based upon the given conditions. If your answer is yes, name the theorem or postulate abbreviation to justify your answer.

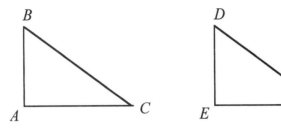

(a) $\angle A \cong \angle E; \angle B \cong \angle D; \overline{AB} \cong \overline{ED}$ _____

(b) $\angle A$ and $\angle E$ are right angles; $\overline{BC} \cong \overline{DF}; \angle C \cong \angle F$ _____

(c) $\overline{AC} \cong \overline{EF}; \angle C \cong \angle F; \overline{BC} \cong \overline{DF}$ _____

(d) $\overline{AC} \cong \overline{EF}; \overline{BC} \cong \overline{DF}; \overline{AB} \cong \overline{ED}$ _____

2. In each of the parts, there is at least one pair of congruent triangles. Identify them and tell why they are congruent.

(a)

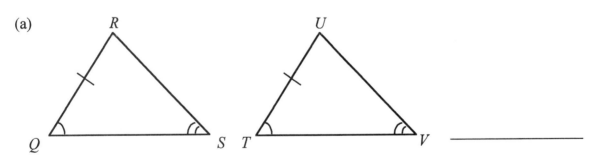

(b)

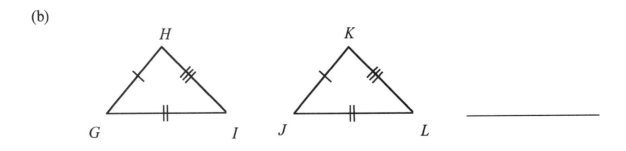

(c)

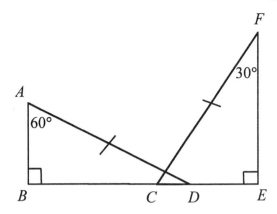

3. Construct each of the following using any tool.

   (a)   Angle bisector of ∠ A

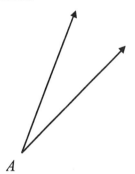

   (b)   Perpendicular bisector of $\overline{AB}$

   (c)   Altitude of △ABC from A

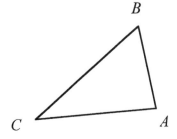

(d)   Parallel to ℓ through m

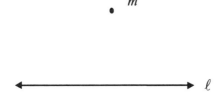

(e)   Divide the given segment into three congruent parts.

_____

A   B

4.   For each of the following pairs of similar triangles, find the missing measure.

(a)

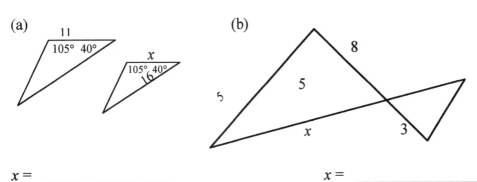

(b)

$x =$ _____

$x =$ _____

(c)

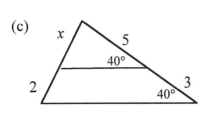

$x =$ _____

5. A person 122 cm tall casts a 37-cm shadow at the same time a tree casts a 148-cm shadow. How tall is the tree? _____

6. Suppose you have three straight sticks of lengths 5 cm, 12 cm, and 19 cm. Can you arrange these sticks into a triangle? If not, why not? _____

7. (a) What kind of figure is quadrilateral *ABCD* as shown below? _____

    (b) Is ∠*GFB* congruent to ∠*FGC*? Justify your answer. _____

    (c) Is ∠*GFB* congruent to ∠*FGD*? Justify your answer. _____

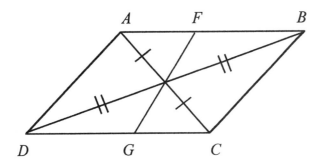

8. Give one example of information that would determine congruency for each of the following.

    (a) Two squares

    (b) Two rhombi

9. $\overline{AD}$ is the perpendicular bisector of $\overline{CB}$. Construct and label three isosceles triangles that have points B and C as two of their vertices.

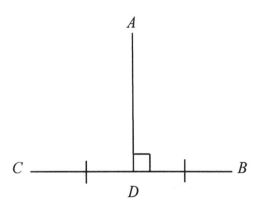

10. (a)   Use only a compass and straight edge to first construct any obtuse angle scalene triangle and then the circle inscribed in the triangle and the circle circumscribing the triangle.

    (b)   In which triangles do the inscribed circle and the circle circumscribing the triangle share the same center? Justify your answer.

11. For each of the following, write the equation of the line determined by the given pair of points.

   (a) $(3, {}^-7)$ and $(3, {}^-27)$ _____

   (b) $({}^-4, 5)$ and $({}^-8, {}^-7)$ _____

12. Determine if the three points with coordinates given lie on the same line. $(2, 3)$, $(4, 6)$ and $(6, 9)$. Explore your answer. _____

13. Find all the solutions of the following systems of equations if possible. If a system has no solution, explain why it does not.

   (a) $3x - y = 3$
       $3x + y = 15$ _____

   (b) $2x - y = 1$
        $2x - 4x = 3$ _____

   (c) $2x - y = 1$
        $2x - 4x = {}^- 2$ _____

1. (a) Yes. *ASA*   (b) Yes. *AAS*   (c) Yes. *SAS*   (d) Yes. *SSS*

2. (a) $\Delta QRS \cong \Delta TUV$ by AAS.
    (b) $\Delta GHI \cong \Delta JKL$ by SSS.
    (c) $\Delta ABD \cong \Delta CEF$ by *ASA*. (It must first be determined that $m(\angle FCE)$ is 60°.)

3. Constructions.

4. (a) $\dfrac{55}{16}$ (b) $\dfrac{40}{3}$ (c) $\dfrac{10}{3}$

5. 488 cm

6. No, the length of every side of a triangle must be less than the sum of the lengths of the other two sides. Note that $19 > 5 + 12$.

7. (a) *ABCD* is a parallelogram.
    (b) No, these two angles are supplementary, but not necessarily congruent.
    (c) Yes, these two angles are congruent because they are alternate interior angles of parallel lines.

8. Answers may vary.

    (a) A side on one square is congruent to a side on the other square.
    (b) The diagonals of one rhombus are correspondingly congruent to the diagonals of the other rhombus.

9. Any triangle with its third vertex on $\overrightarrow{AD}$ is isosceles.

10. (a) Construction   (b) An equilateral triangle, because then the angle bisectors are also the perpendicular bisectors of the sides.

11. (a) $x = 3$ (b) $y = 3x - 1$

12. The points are all on the same line with slope $\dfrac{3}{2}$.

13. (a) $x = 3, y = 6$
    (b) No solution, the lines have the same slope 2 and hence are parallel.
    (c) Infinitely many solutions (the two equations represent the same line), x can be any real number and $y = 2x - 1$.

Sample Assessment

1. Assume that each pair of triangles is congruent and write an appropriate symbolic congruence in each case.

    (a)   (b)

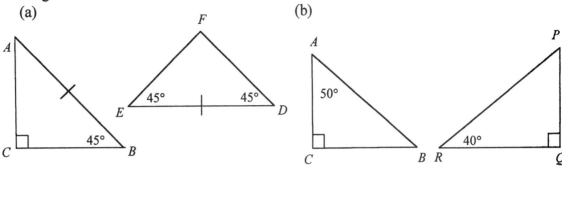

    _____   _____

2. Using only a compass and a straight edge, construct each of the following:

    (a)   An equilateral triangle.

    (b)   A 75° angle.

    (c)   Draw any segment and label it $\overline{AB}$. Then divide it into 3 congruent parts.

(d)   A circle that passes through P and is tangent to ℓ and m where $\ell \| m$.

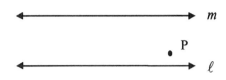

(e)   Given $\triangle ABC$ below, construct a similar triangle whose sides are twice as great.

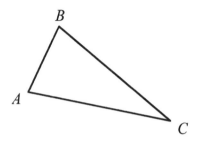

3. Given $\overline{AM} \cong \overline{MC}$ and $\overline{BM} \cong \overline{MD}$ why are the following true? Justify your answer.

(a) $\overline{AB} \cong \overline{CD}$
(b) $\overline{AB} \| \overline{CD}$

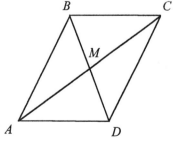

4. In each of the following find x and y if possible.

(a)

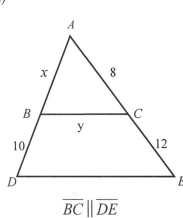

$\overline{BC} \parallel \overline{DE}$

$x =$ _____ $y =$ _____

(b)

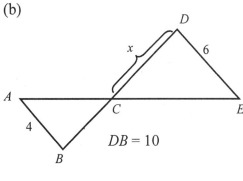

$DB = 10$

$x =$ _____

5. For which of the following figures is it possible to construct a circle that circumscribes the figure, and for which does such a circle not exist? Justify your answers and if a circumscribing circle exists construct the figure and its circumscribing circle.

(a) a rectangle _____

(b) an isosceles trapezoid _____

(c) a rhombus which is not a square _____

6. Answer question 5 for an inscribed circle.

7.   A girl wants to calculate the height of her family's teepee. She is 112 cm tall and she finds that when she is inside and stands so that her head touches the side, her feet are 64 cm from the edge. If the teepee is a right circular cone with a diameter of 352 cm, what is its height?

8.   In each of the following answer true or false. Justify your answers.

(a)   Congruent triangles are also similar. _____

(b)   Two similar triangles are also congruent triangles. _____

(c)   Any two equilateral triangles are similar. _____

(d)   Two isosceles triangles are similar. _____

(e)   The diagonals of a trapezoid divide it into four triangles, two of which are similar. _____

(f)   If three sides of one triangle are parallel, respectively, to three sides of a second triangle, then the triangles are similar. _____

9.   Suppose you have three straight sticks of lengths 10 cm, 20 cm, and 31 cm. Can you arrange these sticks into a triangle? If not, why not? _____

10. Two lines are parallel if they have the same slope. Explain why the points with the following coordinates form a parallelogram.

$A(3, 4), B(5, 8), C(8, 3), D(6, ^-1)$

11. Write the equation of $\overleftrightarrow{AB}$ from problem 10.

12. Solve each of the following systems of equations graphically, if possible. Indicate whether the system has a unique solution, infinitely many solutions, or no solution.

(a) $3y = x - 10$
     $y = x - 2$

(b) $x + y = 5$
     $3x + 3y = 15$

1. (a) $\triangle ABC \cong \triangle EDF$ (b) $\triangle ABC \cong \triangle PRQ$

2. Constructions.

    (d)   If the distance between the lines is d, the radius of the required circle is d/2. The center of the circle is on the line k parallel to m and at the distance d/2 from m and from ℓ. To locate the center, draw an arc with center at P and radius d/2; the points of intersection of the arc width k are the possible centers of the required circle. There are two such circles.

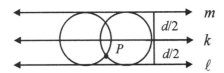

3. (a)   Follows from $\triangle AMB \cong \triangle CMD$ which are congruent by *SAS*.
    (b)   From $\triangle AMB \cong \triangle CMB$ it follows that $\angle BAM \cong \angle DCM$ and hence that $\overline{AB} \mid\mid \overline{CD}$.

4. (a) $x = \dfrac{20}{3}$; y cannot be determined from the given data.
    (b) $x = 6$

5. In (a) and (b), the perpendicular bisectors of the sides intersect in a single point that is the center of the circumscribing circle for the given figure. In a rhombus which is not a square, the four perpendicular bisectors are not concurrent (do not intersect in a single point).

6. Only in a rhombus are the angle bisectors of the four angles concurrent since the diagonals of a rhombus are also its angle bisectors.

7. 308 cm

8. (a)   True by *AA*.
    (b)   False. In similar triangles the ratio between corresponding sides does not have to be 1.
    (c)   True by *AA* since all the angles have measure 60°.
    (d)   False. Two isosceles triangles may have noncongruent base angles.
    (e)   True. $\triangle BCE \sim \triangle DAE$ by *AA*; $\angle CBE \cong \angle EDA$ as they are alternate interior angles between the parallels $\overleftrightarrow{BC}$ and $\overleftrightarrow{AD}$ and the transversal $\overleftrightarrow{BD}$, and the angles at E are congruent as vertical angles.

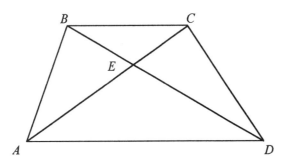

(f)   True. If two sides of one angle are parallel respectively to two sides of a second angle, the angles must be congruent. (If a proof is desired extend two non-parallel sides of the angles and use corresponding angles to show that the angles are congruent.) Consequently the statement follows by *AA*.

9. No, the length of any side of a triangle must be less than the sum of the lengths of the other two sides. Note that $31 > 10 + 20$.

10. The slope of $\overleftrightarrow{AB}$ is 2; the slope of $\overleftrightarrow{BC}$ is $\dfrac{^-5}{3}$; the slope of $\overleftrightarrow{DC}$ is 2; and the slope of $\overleftrightarrow{AD}$ is $\dfrac{^-5}{3}$. Thus, $\overleftrightarrow{AB} \parallel \overleftrightarrow{CD}$ and $\overleftrightarrow{BC} \parallel \overleftrightarrow{AD}$. Therefore $ABCD$ is a parallelogram.

11. $y = 2x - 2$.

12. (a)   The unique solution is $x = {}^-2, y = {}^-4$.

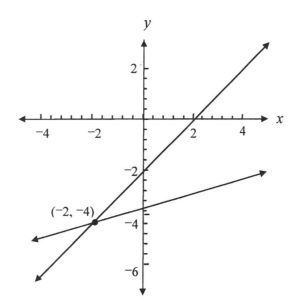

(b) The second equation is equivalent to the first (multiply both sides of the first equation by 3). Hence the graphs of each equation is the same straight line and the system has infinitely many solutions: x can be any real number and $y = 5 - x$.

Sample Assessment

1. Complete the following table converting metric measures.

	mm	cm	m	km
(a)		5,200		
(b)			260	
(c)				0.3
(d)	1,300,000			

2. Find the area of each of the following.

(a)

10 m, 26 m

$A =$ _____

(b)

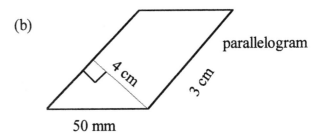

parallelogram

4 cm

3 cm

50 mm

$A =$ _____

3. Find the surface area of a square prism whose base has a side of length 5 cm and a height of 6 cm.

S.A. = _____

4. Find the area of the shaded region on the following geoboard if the unit of measurement is 1 cm^2.

$A =$ _____

5. If a square has the area 10 cm^2, what is the length of a side? _____

6. Explain how the formula for the area of a triangle can be determined by using the formula for the area of a parallelogram.

7. Answer the following.

(a) If the volume of a sphere is $\dfrac{500\pi}{3}$ m³, what is the diameter of the sphere? _____

(b) Find the volume of a cylinder whose height is 2 m and whose base has an area of 9π m². _____

8. What is the area of the figure below? The arc shown is a semicircle.

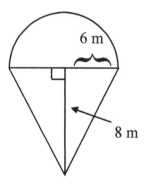

6 m

8 m

9. For each of the following, can the measures represent sides of a right triangle? Explain your answers.

(a) 3 m, 4 m, 5 m _____

(b) $\sqrt{2}$ cm, $\sqrt{3}$ cm, $\sqrt{5}$ cm _____

10. Complete each of the following:

(a) 500 cm² = _____ m²   (b) 18 km = _____ m
(c) 4000 g = _____ kg   (d) 300 mL = _____ L
(e) 17 ha = _____ m²   (f) 0.027 kL = _____ mL
(g) 0.027 L = _____ cm³   (h) 4738 kL of water at 4°C has a mass of _____ kg.

11. Complete the following: (Use a calculator whenever convenient.)

    (a) 1400 ft^2 = _____ yd^2 (b) 1/9 yd^3 = _____ ft^3

    (c) 4.5 lb = _____ oz   (d) 32°C = _____ °F

12. (a) Suppose one edge of a cubic tank is 8 m and the tank is filled with water at 4°C; find the volume of the tank in cubic meters. _____

    (b) Find the capacity of the tank of (a) in liters. _____

    (c) Find the mass of the water of (a) in kilograms. _____

13. Complete each of the following.

    (a) 3 dm^3 of water has a mass of _____ g.
    (b) 2 L of water has a mass of _____ g.
    (c) 13 cm^3 of water has a mass of _____ g.
    (d) 4.2 L of water has a mass of _____ g.
    (e) 3.01 L of water has a volume of _____ m^3.

14. Find the volume of a cone whose slant height is 50 cm and whose height is 40 cm. _____

15. If the diameter of a circle is 14 cm, find each of the following.

    (a) the circumference of the circle _____

    (b) the area of the circle _____

    (c) the area of a sector of the circle that corresponds to a central angle of 18°. _____

16. Find the perimeter of the following if all arcs shown are semicircles. _____

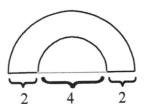

2   4   2

1.

	mm	cm	m	km
(a)	52,000	5,200	52	0.052
(b)	260,000	26,000	260	0.260
(c)	300,000	30,000	300	0.3
(d)	1,300,000	130,000	1,300	1.3

2. (a) 120 m^2 (b) 12 cm^2

3. 170 cm^2

4. 8 cm^2

5. $\sqrt{10}$ cm

6. Given any triangle ABC as shown, another triangle $A'B'C'$ can be constructed and placed to form parallelogram $ABA'C$. The area of parallelogram $ABA'C$ is bh. Thus, the area of $\triangle ABC$ is $\dfrac{1}{2}bh$.

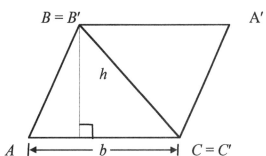

7. (a) 10 m   (b) 18π m^3

8. $(48 + 18\pi)$ m^2

9. (a) Yes. $3^2 + 4^2 = 5^2$

   (b) Yes. $(\sqrt{2})^2 + (\sqrt{3})^2 = (\sqrt{5})^2$

10. (a) 0.05   (b) 18,000   (c) 4
    (d) 0.3   (e) 170,000   (f) 27,000
    (g) 27   (h) 4,738,000

11. (a) 155.$\overline{5}$ (b) 3   (c) 72   (d) 89.6

12. (a) 512 m^3 (b) 512,000 L   (c) 512,000 kg

13. (a) 3000   (b) 2000

   (c)   13   (d)   4200

   (e)   0.00301

14. $12{,}000\pi\,\text{cm}^3$

15. (a) $14\pi\,\text{cm}$ (b) $49\pi\,\text{cm}^2$ (c) $(49/20)\,\pi\,\text{cm}^2$ or $2.45\pi\,\text{cm}^2$

16. $6\pi + 4$

Sample Assessment

1. Complete the following table converting metric measures.

	mm	cm	m	km
(a)		500		
(b)			26	
(c)				0.001
(d)	1,500			

2. Find the area of $\triangle ABC$ in each of the following.

(a)   (b)

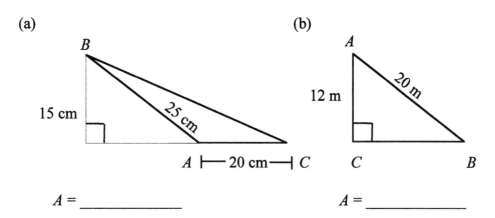

$A =$ _____ $A =$ _____

3. Assume that the only area formula you know is the formula for the area of a triangle. Explain how to derive the formula for the area of a trapezoid.

4. A toy manufacturer wants to design a wooden square pyramid whose volume is 8000 cm^3.

   (a) Design such a pyramid. Make a sketch and show the dimensions of the base and the altitude.

   (b) How many such pyramids are possible? _____ Why?

5. If each dimension of a box is quadrupled, how are the surface area and the volume affected?

6. For each of the following, can the measures represent sides of a right triangle? Explain your answers.

    (a) 30 cm, 40 cm, 50 cm _____

    (b) (b) $\sqrt{2}$ cm, $\sqrt{3}$ cm, $\sqrt{6}$ cm _____

7. A rectangular prism has dimensions 60 cm, 40 cm, 200 cm.

    (a)   Find the surface area of the prism in square centimeters. _____

    (b)   Find the volume of the prism in cubic meters. _____

    (c)   Find the capacity of the prism in liters _____

8. A cone has a circular base with radius 50 cm and slant height 90 cm. Find the surface area.

    _____

9. A box-shaped container has a 2 m by 3 m rectangular base. It is partially filled with water and the height of the water is 0.5 m.

    (a)   How many liters of water are in the container? _____ L

    (b)   Find the mass of the water in kilograms. _____ kg

    (c)   If 60 L of water are added to the container, how much will the water rise? _____ m

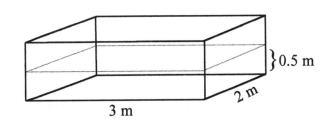

10. Find the surface area of a right circular cylinder that is 6 cm in diameter and is 12 cm in height. _____

11. Solve for x in each of the following:

(a)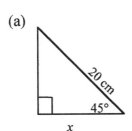

(b)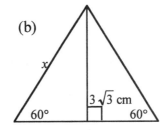

(c)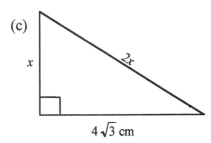

(a) $x =$ _____   (b) $x =$ _____   (c) $x =$ _____

12. Complete the following: (Use a calculator whenever convenient.)

    (a) $30 \text{ m}^2 =$ _____ cm^2

    (b) $0.03 \text{ L} =$ _____ mL

    (c) $3 \text{ yd}^2 =$ _____ ft^2

    (d) $48{,}033 \text{ ft}^3 =$ _____ yd^3

    (e) $10 \text{ ha} =$ _____ m^2

    (f) $-40°\text{C} =$ _____ $°\text{F}$

13. What happens to the surface area of a sphere if the diameter is tripled?

14. Find the volume of the figure below (assume a right circular cylinder on bottom and half of a sphere on top).

    $V =$ _____

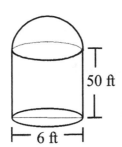

1.

	mm	cm	m	km
(a)	5,000	5,00	5	0.005
(b)	26,000	2,600	26	0.026
(c)	1,000	100	1	0.001
(d)	1,500	150	1.5	0.0015

2. (a) 150 cm^2 (b) 96 m^2

3.   Use a diagonal of a trapezoid to divide it into two triangles as shown below. The height of each triangle is the same. The area of one triangle is $\frac{1}{2} b_1 h$ and area of the other triangle is $\frac{1}{2} b_2 h$. Hence the area of the trapezoid is $\frac{1}{2} h(b_1 + b_2)$.

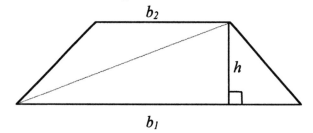

4.   (a)

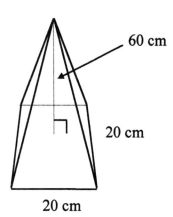

60 cm

20 cm

20 cm

   (b)   There are infinitely many possible pyramids. If s is the length of the side of the base and h the height of the pyramid, then the volume of the pyramid is $(1/3)s^2h$. We have $(1/3)s^2h = 8000$ or $h = 24,000/s^2$. Thus, we may assign s an arbitrary value and obtain a corresponding value for h.

5.   The surface area is 16 times as great; the volume is 64 times as great.

6. (a) Yes. $50^2 = 30^2 + 40^2$ (b)   No. $\left(\sqrt{6}\right)^2 \neq \left(\sqrt{2}\right)^2 + \left(\sqrt{3}\right)^2$

7. (a) $44,800 \text{ cm}^2$ (b) 0.48 m^3 (c)   480 L

8. $7000\pi\,\text{cm}^2$

9. (a)   3000 L   (b)   3000 kg   (c)   1 cm or 0.01 m

10. $90\pi\,\text{cm}^2$ or approximately 282.7 cm^2

11. (a) $10\sqrt{2}$ cm or approximately 14.14 cm   (b)   6 cm   (c)   4 cm

12. (a)   300,000   (b)   30   (c)   27
     (d)   1779   (e)   100,000   (f) $^-40$

13. It is nine times greater.

14. $468\,\pi\,\text{ft}^3$ or approximately 1470.3 ft^3

Sample Assessment

1. Complete each of the following motions.

(a)

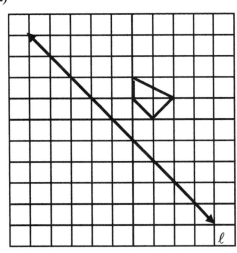

a reflection in ℓ

(b)

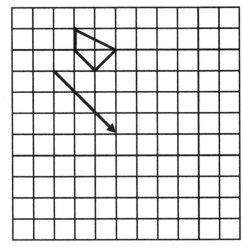

a translation as pictured

(c)

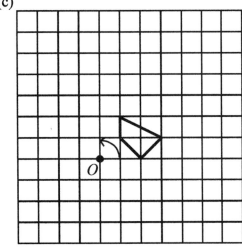

a rotation in O through
the given arc

(d)

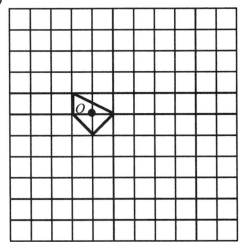

a size transformation with
center O and scale factor 2

2. How many lines of symmetry, if any, does each of the following figures have?

(a)

(b)

3. The following pairs of figures are congruent. Tell which transformations will take figure (1) to figure (2).

(a)

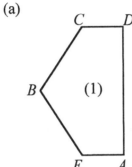

(b)

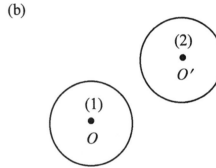

4. For each of the following transformations, construct the image of $\overline{AB}$.

(a)   A reflection in ℓ

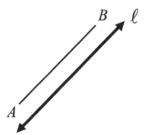

(b)   A translation which takes M to N

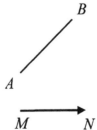

(c)   A rotation in O as indicated

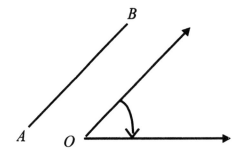

5. Describe objects that have each of the following types of symmetry.

   (a)   line

   (b)   point

   (c)   plane

   (d)   90° rotational

6. For each of the following pairs of figures, determine which transformation might take one figure to the other.

   (a)

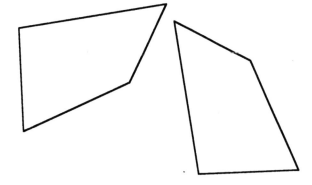

(b)

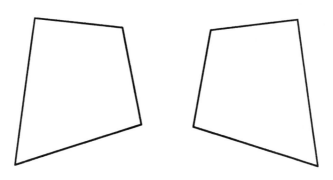

(c)

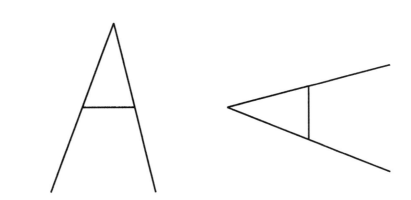

7. (a) Draw a rectangle *ABCD* and then construct a line such that the image of the rectangle under reflection in the line is the original rectangle. Is there more than one line with this property?

   (b) For what kind of rectangles is it possible to find more than two lines with the property in (a). Justify your answer.

   (c) Describe all trapezoids for which it is possible to find a line ℓ such that when the trapezoid is reflected in ℓ its image is itself.

8. (a)   Find the image of the circle with center O under a size transformation with scale factor $\dfrac{3}{4}$.

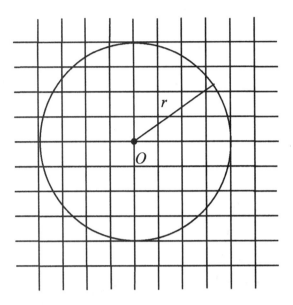

   (b)   What kind of figure is the image in (a)? Why?

9. Show that the circle with center O' is the image of the circle with center O under a succession of isometries with a size transformation.

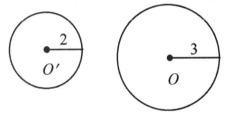

10. If possible, describe a geometric figure that can be transformed into itself by each of the following:

   (a)   reflection

   (b)   rotation

   (c)   translation

   (d)   glide reflection

11. Use a reflection to argue that the base angles of an isosceles triangle are congruent.

12. Given points A and B and $\triangle DEF$ below, find point C on $\triangle DEF$ such that $\triangle ABC$ is isosceles.

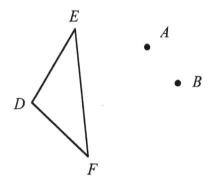

13. Let ℓ' be the image of ℓ under a half-turn about point O. If A' is the image of A and B' the image of B and $\overline{OB} \perp \ell$, classify each of the following as true or false. Justify your answers.

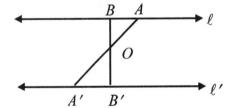

_____(a) $\triangle OAB \cong \triangle OA'B'$

_____(b) OB' is the distance from O to ℓ'.

_____(c) $\ell || \ell'$

_____(d)   The image of $\overline{AA'}$ is $\overline{BB'}$.

14. A student claims that anything that can be accomplished by a translation can also be accomplished by a reflection. She claims that if A' is the image of A under a translation, then A' can be obtained by a reflection in the line ℓ which is the perpendicular bisector of $\overline{AA'}$. Hence, a translation and a reflection are the same. How do you respond?

15. Find the images of the points $P(^-3, 4)$ and $Q(a,b)$ under each of the following transformations.

    _____ (i)   Translation given by $(x,y) \rightarrow (x + 3, y - 4)$
    _____ (ii)   Reflection in the line $y = x$
    _____ (iii) Reflection in the line $y = -x$
    _____ (iv)   Half turn about the origin
    _____ (v)   Rotation by 90° counterclockwise about the origin.

16. Find the point whose image is $(^-3, 4)$ and the point whose image is (a, b) under each of the transformations in problem 15.

*17. Explain why a regular pentagon cannot tessellate the plane.

*18. Explain with a drawing whether or not you think the *H*-shape below is a good shape for a commercial cookie maker.

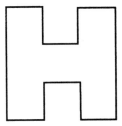

1. (a)

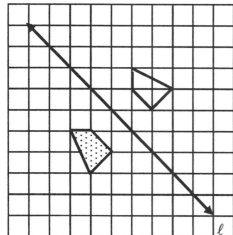

(b)

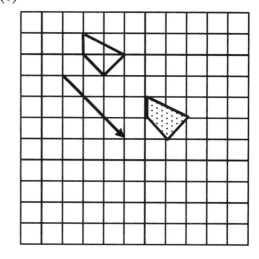

(c)

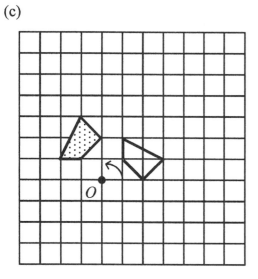

(d)

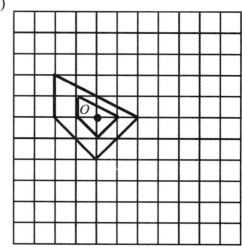

2. (a)   6   (b)   3

3. (a)   Reflection or half turn
   (b)   Slide, reflection, or half turn

4. (a)   (b)   (c)

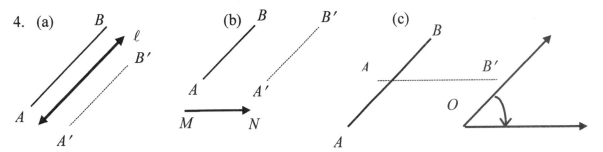

5. Answers may vary. For example,
   (a)   An isosceles triangle   (b)   An equilateral triangle
   (c)   A right circular cylinder   (d)   A square

6. (a)   Rotation   (b)   Reflection   (c)   Rotation

7. (a)   A line which is the perpendicular bisector of any pair of opposite sides has the
         property.
   (b)   For squares. Because the diagonals of a square are perpendicular bisectors of each
         other, the lines containing the diagonals have the required property. Hence a square
         has four such lines.
   (c)   Isosceles trapezoids.

8. (a)

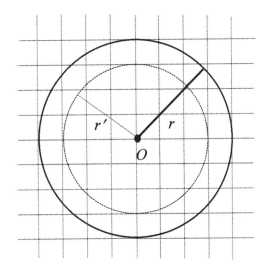

   (b)   The figure is a circle with center O and radius $\frac{3}{4}r$ because the image of every point is

         a point which is $\frac{3}{4}r$ away from O.

9. One way is to apply the following transformations in succession: a translation from O to O',

   and a size transformation with center O' and scale factor $\frac{2}{3}$.

10. Answers may vary. For example,
    (a)   Rectangle   (b)   Square   (c)   Parallel lines   (d)   Parallel lines

11. Hint: Use the angle bisector of the non-base angle as a reflecting line.

12. Hint: Use the perpendicular bisector of $\overline{AB}$. There are two such points.

13. (a)   True. $\Delta OAB \cong \Delta O'A'B'$ by SAS since $\overline{OA} \cong \overline{O'A'}$, $\overline{OB} \cong \overline{O'B'}$ and the angles at O are vertical angles.

  (b)   True. From (a) by CPCTC $\angle OB'A' \cong \angle OBA$ and hence $\angle OB'A'$ is a right angle. Because $\overline{OB} \cong \overline{O'B'}$ and $\overline{OB'} \perp \ell'$, OB' is the distance from O to ℓ'.

  (c)   True. The angles $\angle OB'A' \cong \angle OBA$ are alternate interior and congruent angles between ℓ and ℓ' and the transversal $\overleftrightarrow{BB'}$.

  (d)   False. The image of $\overleftrightarrow{AA'}$ is $\overleftrightarrow{AA'}$.

14. What the student says is true for a single point, but not for the entire plane. For example, if B is on ℓ, then B', the image of B under the translation, is not the reflection of B in ℓ.

15. (a) $P'(0, 0)$, $Q'(a + 3, b - 4)$ (b) $P'(4, -3)$, $Q'(b, a)$

  (c) $P'(-4, 3)$, $Q'(-b, -a)$ (d) $P'(3, -4)$, $Q'(-a, -b)$

  (e) $P'(-4, -3)$, $Q'(-b, a)$

16. (a) $(-6, 8)$, $(a - 3, b + 4)$ (b) $(4, -3)$, (b, a)

  (c) $(-4, 3)$, $(-b, -a)$ (d) $(3, -4)$, $(-a, -b)$

  (e) $(4, 3)$, $(b, -a)$

17. The measure of each interior angle in a regular pentagon is $\dfrac{3 \cdot 180°}{5}$ or 108°. Because 360 is not divisible by 108, a regular pentagon cannot tessellate the plane.

18. The shape can tessellate the plane and would be a good shape for a commercial cookie maker. Some dough would be lost at the top and bottom as seen below.

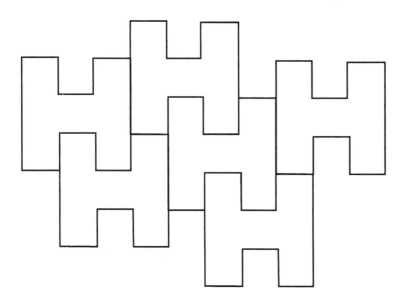

Sample Assessment

1. Complete each of the following motions.

(a)

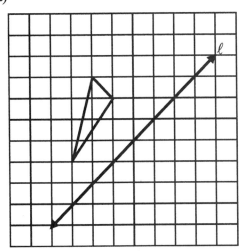

a reflection in ℓ

(b)

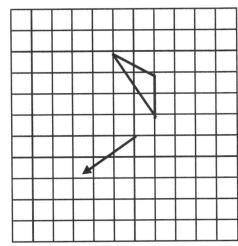

a translation as pictured

(c)

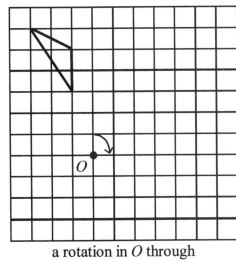

a rotation in O through
the given arc

(d)

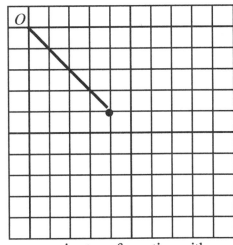

a size transformation with
center O and scale factor 1/2

2. For each of the following transformations construct the image of the indicated figure.

   (a)   A reflection of $\triangle ABC$ in ℓ

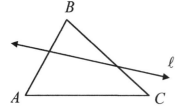

   (b)   A translation of the circle along the arrow from M to N.

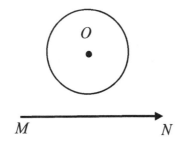

   (c)   A half-turn of the line ℓ in O.

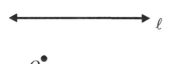

(d) A 60° rotation counterclockwise of △ABC in A.

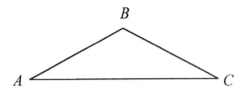

3. How many lines of symmetry, if any, does each of the following figures have?

(a)

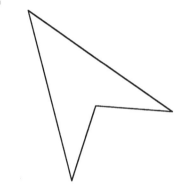

_____

(b)

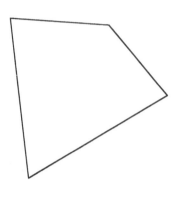

_____

(c)

_____

(d)

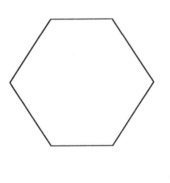

_____

4. Describe point symmetry and rotational symmetries, if any, of the parts of Problem 3.

5. For each of the following pairs of figures, determine which transformation might take one figure to the other.

    (a)

    (b)
    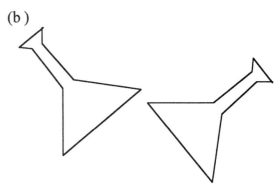

    (c)

    (d)
    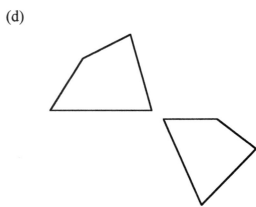

6. Find the minimum number of reflecting lines needed to accomplish the isometries in Problem 5.

    (a) _____   (b) _____   (c) _____   (d) _____

7. Use a reflection to argue that the base angles of an isosceles trapezoid are congruent.

8. Show that $\triangle ADE$ is the image of $\triangle ABC$ under a succession of isometries with a size transformation.

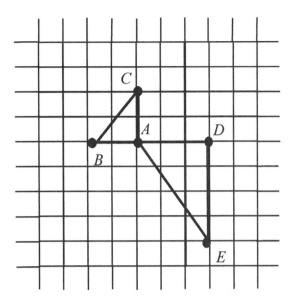

9. A student claims that anything that can be accomplished by a glide reflection can also be accomplished by a half-turn. He claims that if A' is the image of A under a glide reflection then A' can also be obtained by a half-turn about point O, where O is the intersection of the line of reflection with $\overline{AA'}$. Hence a glide reflection and a half-turn are the same. How do you respond?

10. A student claims that a succession of two reflections in two perpendicular lines can always be accomplished by a half-turn. Hence a secession of two reflections in two perpendicular lines is a half-turn. How do you respond?

11. Find the images of the points $P(2, 3)$ and $Q(a, b)$ under each of the following:

    (a)   Translation given by $(x, y) \rightarrow (x + 3, y + 5)$

    (b)   Translation given in (a) followed by the same translation

(c)   Reflection in the line $y = 0$

(d)   Reflection in the line $x = 0$

(e)   Reflection in the line $y = 0$ followed by a reflection in line $x = 0$

12. Write a word that has only a vertical line of symmetry.

_____

13. If given two parallel lines, describe a motion that can make one line the image of the other.

*14. What regular figure can be used with a regular octagon to tessellate the plane?

*15. Show how the figure below might be used to tessellate the plane.

* 16. Show how to tessellate the plane with the quadrilateral given below.

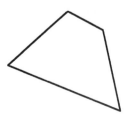

1. (a)

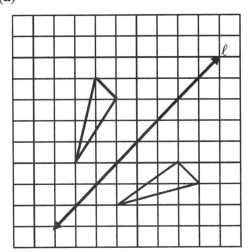

(b)

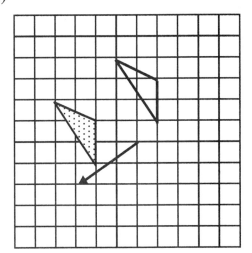

(c)

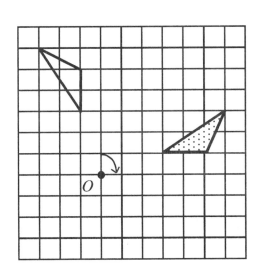

(d)

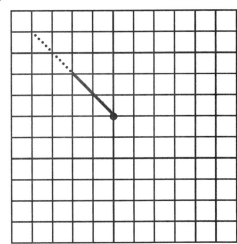

Original is dotted. Image is solid.

2. (a)

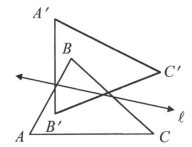

(b)

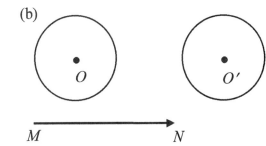

2. (cont.)

(c)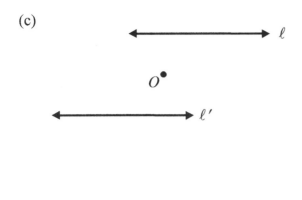

(d)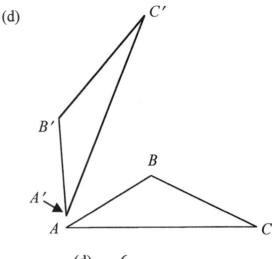

3. (a) 1 (b) 1 (c) 5 (d) 6

4. (a) Neither
   (b) Neither
   (c) Rotational symmetries of 72°, 144°, 216°, 288°
   (d) Rotational symmetries of 60°, 120°, 180°, 240°, 300°; also has point symmetry

5. (a) Reflection (b) Reflection
   (c) Translation (d) Rotation

6. (a) 1 (b) 1 (c) 2 (d) 2

7. Hint: Use the line through the midpoints of parallel sides. The image of one of the base angles should be the other.

8. Find the image of $\triangle ABC$ under a translation from B to A. Then apply to this image a reflection in the line $\overleftrightarrow{BA}$. Finally apply a size transformation with center A and a scale factor of 2.

9. What the student says is true for a single point, but not for the entire plane, or even two points. If B' is the image of $B(B \neq A)$ under the same glide reflection, then the intersection of the line of the reflection with $\overline{BB'}$ is different than O.

10. The student is correct. The half-turn is about the point of intersection of the perpendicular lines ℓ and m. If the lines intersect at O, then A' is the reflection of A in ℓ, A'' is the reflection of A' in m, and A''' is the reflection of A'' in ℓ. Then A, A', A'' and A''' are vertices of a rectangle. Because the diagonals of a rectangle bisect each other at O, A'' is the image of A under a half-turn in O.

10. (cont.)

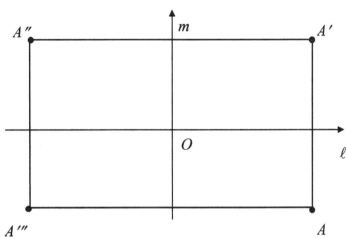

11. (a) $P'(5, 8)$, $Q'(a + 3, b + 5)$
    (b) $P''(8, 13)$, $Q''(a + 6, b + 10)$
    (c) $P'(2, -3)$, $Q'(a, -b)$
    (d) $P'(-2, 3)$, $Q'(-a, b)$
    (e) $P'(-2, -3)$, $Q'(-a, -b)$

12. Answers will vary. For example, MOM.

13. Answers may vary. Perhaps the easiest is a translation with slide arrow having one end point on one line and the other on the other line.

14. A square with a side the same length as a side of the octagon.

*15. One method is illustrated below.

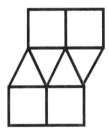

*16. Hint: Try half-turns of the figure about midpoints of the sides.

Chapter 1

In the class elections, there were five candidates for class president. The teachers decided to help guarantee a fair election by having a series of head-to-head elections in which each candidate ran against each other candidate. The class president is the person who won the most head-to-head elections. You are asked to determine how many elections are needed.

With five candidates, A, B, C, D, and E, each having to run against the other, we could list all of the possible elections as follows:

A–B	B–C	C–D	D–E
A–C	B–D	C–E	
A–D	B–E		
A–E			

Thus, there are $4 + 3 + 2 + 1$, or 10 elections required.

Chapter 2

Consider the set of 38 toppings excluding mushroom and cheese. This set has 2^{38} subsets. Putting the two excluded toppings in each of the subsets will result in 2^{38} subsets each of that will include mushroom and cheese toppings. We can use a calculator to compute 2^{38} or estimate that number as follows:

$$2^{38} = 2^{10} \cdot 2^{10} \cdot 2^{10} \cdot 2^{8}$$

Because $2^{10} = 1024$ and $2^{8} = 256$ we have

$$2^{38} > 1000 \cdot 1000 \cdot 1000 \cdot 256$$

Thus, 2^{38} is greater than 256 billion, a number greater than the population of the world that is approximately 6 billion. Thus, the ad is truthful.

Chapter 3

There are 85 members of a PTA to contact using a phone chain. We are to assume that each call takes 30 seconds and that everyone is at home and answers the phone. The key to solving this problem is to realize that when caller calls one of his/her two people, the first person being called does not wait for the second person to be called before this first person can begin calling his/her two people. A strategy is to build a model of this phone tree and a table to keep track of

Chapter 3 (cont.)

the number of people contacted. A model for the first 3 min. is given below. The table on the right of the model shows the number of *People called* in each 30-second interval and it also shows the *Total number called*.

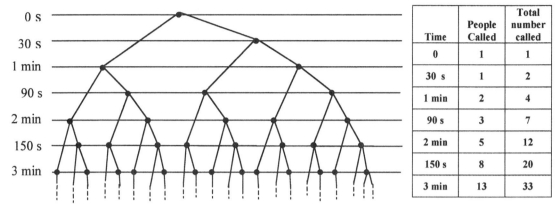

Time	People Called	Total number called
0	1	1
30 s	1	2
1 min	2	4
90 s	3	7
2 min	5	12
150 s	8	20
3 min	13	33

If we examine the numbers in the *People Called* column, we notice a familiar sequence, that is, the *Fibonacci* sequence where each number in the sequence is the sum of the previous two numbers. We can see from the model that this will continue to happen because the number of dots in each segment is the sum of the dots in the previous two segments. Therefore, we need to continue the table to see at what time the total number of people called reaches or exceeds 85. Continuing the table we see that there would be $8 + 13 = 21$ more people called at 210 s giving a total of $33 + 21 = 54$. For 4 min., there would be $13 + 21 = 34$ more people called giving a total of $54 + 34 = 88$. Therefore we can call 85 people in 4 min.

We can extend the problem by trying different numbers of members of the PTA or generalizing the problem to finding the length of time required to call *n* people. We could also investigate how the Fibonacci sequence shows up in other contexts such as pine cones, or the breeding habits of some animals.

Chapter 4

Assuming that the ages are whole numbers, we list the decompositions of 36 into three factors each followed by the sum of the three factors.

$1 \cdot 1 \cdot 36$ 38

$1 \cdot 3 \cdot 12$ 16

$1 \cdot 2 \cdot 18$ 21

$1 \cdot 4 \cdot 9$ 14

$1 \cdot 6 \cdot 6$ **13**

$2 \cdot 2 \cdot 9$ **13**

$2 \cdot 3 \cdot 6$ 11

$4 \cdot 3 \cdot 3$ 10

Chapter 4 (cont.)

The only sum of three factors that occurs more than once is indicated in bold. If all sums were different, Tira would have known which one it is, because she was told that the "right" sum is her street address. Because she needed more information, we can conclude that the ages of Ben's children are 1, 6, 6, or 2, 2, 9. Ben's reply that his oldest child is a girl eliminates the 1, 6, 6 possibility for the ages because there is no oldest child among these ages. Hence, the children's ages must be 2, 2, and 9.

Chapter 5

After 12 o'clock, the two hands first point in opposite directions at $32\frac{8}{11}$ minutes after 12, and at intervals of 1 hr, $5\frac{5}{11}$ minutes after that. The times between 12:00 and 1:00 are 12: $32\frac{8}{11}$, 1: $38\frac{2}{11}$, 2: $43\frac{7}{11}$, 3: $49\frac{1}{11}$, 4: $54\frac{6}{11}$, 7: $5\frac{5}{11}$, 8: $10\frac{10}{11}$, 9: $16\frac{4}{11}$, 10: $21\frac{9}{11}$, and 11: $27\frac{3}{11}$. Other times are possible by continuing to add 1 hr, $5\frac{5}{11}$ minutes to the times.

Chapter 6

Because the player has missed 23 of 137 attempts, she has made 114 shots. She will get at least 40 more attempts so she will end the season with at least 177 attempts. We need to determine if there is some number less than or equal to 40 such that when we add it to 114 and divide by 177, the percentage is greater than or equal to 77%.

$$\frac{114 + x}{177} \geq \frac{77}{100}$$

$$(114 + x)100 \geq 77(177)$$

$$11{,}400 + 100x \geq 13{,}629$$

$$100x \geq 13{,}629 - 11{,}400 = 2229$$

$$x \geq \frac{2229}{100} \text{ or } 22.29.$$

Therefore, she needs to make at least 23 of her 40 attempts to shoot a percentage greater than or equal to 77%.

We could also investigate what the highest or lowest percentage she could reach would be and we could vary the number of attempts that she will have.

Chapter 7

Following the hint for solving the Preliminary Problem, we first find the probability that all 40 children have different birthdays and then subtract the result from 1. We get

$$1 - (\frac{365-1}{365})(\frac{365-2}{365}) \cdots (\frac{365-39}{365}) \doteq 0.891$$

Thus, the probability that the friend wins the bet is approximately 0.891 or 89.1%. For 50 people, the probability rises to approximately 0.97.

A different approach to solving the problem is to think about it as an occupancy problem where the names of 40 children are randomly put in 365 boxes, one box for each day of the year. The sample space S is the set of all permutations of 365 possible birthdays (repetition allowed). Thus, S has 365^{40} elements. The number of elements in the event that at least two children have the same birthday is 365^{40} minus the number of elements in the event that all birthdays are different, that is:

$$\frac{365^{40} - 365 \cdot 364 \cdot \ldots \cdot (365-39)}{365^{40}} .$$

This expression can of course be written in the form found in the first approach.

Chapter 8

We know the sum of the ages of the first seven guests divided by 7 is 21. Therefore, the sum of the ages is $7 \cdot 21 = 147$. If we add another age of 29 to the sum, we have $147 + 29 = 176$. If we divide by 8, we see the mean is now 22. When another 29 year old enters the room, the sum of the ages increases to $176 + 29 = 205$ and we now have nine people. If we let the chair's age be represented by x, then the sum of the ages of the ten people now present is $205 + x$. If we divide this sum by 10, the chair reported we would obtain the mean of 27. If we solve the equation for x, we will have the chair's age.

$$\frac{205 + x}{10} = 27$$

$$205 + x = 270$$

$$x = 65$$

Therefore, the chair is 65 years old.

Chapter 9

The only possible figures that can be used are triangles with acute angles. If a convex polygon has n sides, then it has n exterior angles. The sum of the measures of the exterior angles is 360°. With the exterior and interior angles of the polygon, there are n supplementary angles. The sum of the measures of the n supplementary angles is $180n$. The sum of the measures of the interior angles must be $180n - 360$, or $180(n - 2)$. Thus, n must be greater than or equal to 3. (Why?) Could n be 4 or any number greater than 4, and could all n interior angles be less than 90°? If so, then we have the following:

$$180(n - 2) < 90n$$
$$180n - 360 < 90n$$
$$90n < 360$$
$$n < 4$$

Hence, the only choice for n is 3, and the polygon must be a triangle.

Chapter 10

Because the wires are alternately perpendicular to the hypotenuse $\overline{AB}$ or the side $\overline{BC}$ of the triangle, congruent alternate interior angles formed by parallel lines are created and hence all the triangles whose two sides are wired are similar to $\triangle ABC$ and to each other. In each triangle the ratio between the shorter wired side and the hypotenuse equals $\dfrac{BC}{AB}$ or $\dfrac{4}{5}$. Thus, each wired side other than $\overline{AC}$ is $\dfrac{4}{5}$ of the previous wired side and therefore the length of the wire is:

$6 + 6 \cdot 0.8 + 6 \cdot 0.8^2 + 6 \cdot 0.8^3 + 6 \cdot 0.8^4$ which is approximately 20.17 ft.

Chapter 11

The area of the square is 100 m • 100 m = 10,000 m². We can compute the area of the large circular area and calculate the percentage of the square covered by the large sprinkler. Next we can compute the area of one of the small circles, multiply this by nine, and then compute the percentage of the square covered by the nine smaller sprinklers. We can then compare the percents and make a decision on the two systems.

The radius of the large circle is 50 m. The area of the larger circle is given by $A = \pi r^2 = \pi(50\text{ m})^2 = 2500\,\pi$ m². The fraction of the large square covered by the large sprinkler is $2500\,\pi/10{,}000$, or about 78.5%.

The radius of a small circle is 16 2/3 m. The area of a small circle is $A = \pi(16\ 2/3)^2 = 277.\overline{7}\,\pi$ m² and the area of nine of these small circles is $9 \cdot 277.\overline{7}\,\pi = 2500\,\pi$ m². The fraction of the large square covered by the nine circles is $2500\,\pi/10{,}000$, or about 78.5%.

Chapter 11 (cont.)

Therefore both sprinkler systems cover the same percent of the square field and it does not matter which system is used if the only selection criterion is the amount of land covered by the system.

Related problems include changing the number of circles contained in the square or changing the size of the square. Will the percent always be the same? Changing the shape of the field can also vary the problem.

Chapter 12

In the drawing below, $\triangle AHT \cong \triangle AET$ and $\triangle DEN \cong \triangle DBN$. (Why?) Thus, $HT = ET$, $EN = BN$, and $HT + TE + EN + NB = 2(TE + EN)$. The image length HB is twice the length of the body seen TN or AD because $TN = AD$.

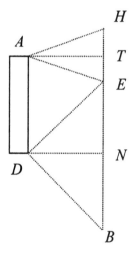

Chapter 1

1. $n^{50} > 2^n$ is not true for $n = 1$ because $1^{50} = 1$ and $2^1 = 2$, but 1 is not greater than 2. Hence, the statement is not true for all values of n in the set of numbers given. Even though the statement is true for $n = 2, 3, \ldots, 50$, we could not conclude that it is true for all values of n greater than 1 because inductive reasoning does not assure the truth of a general statement

2. Since the population is increasing, the ratio of the geometric sequence is greater than 1. Because the terms of such a geometric sequence increase faster than the terms of any arithmetic sequence, it is possible to show that given any increasing geometric sequence and any arithmetic sequence, for some n the nth term of the geometric sequence will be greater than the corresponding term of the arithmetic sequence.

3. The sequence can be thought of as having first term 6 and the fixed difference 0. We can get from one term to the next by adding the same fixed number, namely 0. Therefore this sequence satisfies the definition of an arithmetic sequence.

4. Two terms can lead to more than one sequence. For example, the terms 3, 6, … could lead to 3, 6, 9, 12, … which is an arithmetic sequence with fixed difference 3. It might also lead to 3, 6, 9, 15, 24, 39, … in which each successive term is obtained by adding the two previous terms. Another sequence is 3, 6, 10, 15, 21, … in which the rule is add 3 to the first term, then add 4 to the second term, then add 5 to the third term, and so on. From these examples, we can see that two terms are not enough to determine any sequence.

5. The answer depends upon the responder, but the *Principles and Standards for School Mathematics* (NCTM, 2000) recommend that algebra or algebraic thinking begin from PreK-2.

Chapter 2

1. One way to designate the empty set is { }. Anything we enclose in the braces is an element of the set. Thus, $\{\emptyset\}$ is a set having one element, so it is not empty. The difficulty usually arises from the reluctance to consider the empty set as an element.

2. In fact it is true that $A \cup B = \{a, b, c, d, c, d\}$; however, because the agreement is not to list any element in a set more than once, $\{a, b, c, d, c, \text{d}\} = \{a, b, c, d\}$.

3. The student is right. To show that the hypothesis implies $B = C$ we show that $B \subseteq C$ and $C \subseteq B$. To show that $B \subseteq C$ let $x \in B$, then $x \in A \cup B$ and because $A \cup B = A \cup C$, $x \in A \cup C$. Consequently $x \in A$ or $x \in C$. If $x \in C$ then $B \subseteq C$. If $x \in A$ then since we started with $x \in B$ it follows that $x \in A \cap B$. Because $A \cap B = A \cap C$ we conclude that $x \in A \cap C$ and therefore $x \in C$. Thus $B \subseteq C$. Similarly starting with $x \in C$ it can be shown that $x \in B$ and hence that $C \subseteq B$.

4. No. For example, the set of all rational numbers greater than or equal to 0 and less than or equal to 1 is an infinite set whose greatest element is 1.

Chapter 2 (cont.)

5. The student is incorrect. The student is distributing the complement bar over A and B. The student should be encouraged to check the assertion $\overline{A \cap B} = \overline{A} \cap \overline{B}$ with an example and with a Venn diagram.

6. What the student said is true if $B \subseteq A$ or $B = \varnothing$. However, in general, $\overline{A} \cap \overline{B} \neq \overline{A}$. Consider
   $U = \{1, 2, 3, 4\}$, $A = \{1\}$, and $B = \{2\}$. Here $\overline{A} = \{2, 3, 4\}$ and $\overline{A} \cap \overline{B} = \{3, 4\} \neq \overline{A}$.

7. Since "formula" is not defined, it is really impossible to answer the question. Most likely, students view a formula as a single equation. If this is the case, the concepts are not the same. Students are usually misled by the fact that many functions which appear in mathematical applications are given by equations. However, not every equation represents a function; for example, let $x = y^2$. For every $x \geq 0$, there are two corresponding values of y, and hence the equation does not define a function.

8. The student is wrong. If for example, $A = \{1, 2, 3\}$ and $B = \{2, 3, 4\}$, then neither $A \subseteq B$ nor $B \subseteq A$.

9. Even though the Cartesian product of sets includes all pairings in which each element of the first set is the first component in a pair with each element of the second set, this is not necessarily a one-to-one correspondence. A one-to-one correspondence implies that there must be the same number of elements in each set. This is not the case in Cartesian product. For example, consider sets $A = \{1\}$ and $B = \{a, b\}$.

10. Let $A = \{1, 2, 3\}$ and $B = \{4, 5, 6\}$. The set $\{(1, 4), (2, 5), (3, 6)\}$ is a function from A to B and it is a subset of $A \times B$. However not every subset of $A \times B$ is a function from A to B. For example $(1, 4), (1, 5), (2, 5), (3, 6)\}$ is a subset of $A \times B$ but it is not a function because two different ordered pairs with the same first component are in the set. In general a function from A to B is a subset of $A \times B$ but not every subset of $A \times B$ is a function from A to B.

11. The expressions are not equal because $2 \cdot (3 \cdot 4) = 24$ and $(2 \cdot 3) \cdot (2 \cdot 4) = 6 \cdot 8 = 48$. There is not distributive property of multiplication over multiplication.

12. No. The first equation is true because $39 + 41 = 39 + (1 + 40) = (39 + 1) + 40 = 40 + 40$. Now, $39 \cdot 41 = (40 - 1)(40 + 1) = (40 - 1)\,40 + (40 - 1)1 = 40^2 - 40 + 40 - 1 = 40^2 - 1$, and $40^2 - 1 \neq 40^2$.

13. Yes. If $a < b$, we can write $a = bq + r$ where $q = 0$ and $r = a$. Notice that in this case, we still have $0 \leq r < b$. For example, if $a = 3$ and $b = 5$, then $3 = 0 \cdot 5 + 3$.

Chapter 2 (cont.)

14. By definition $0 \div 0 = x$ if and only if $0 = 0 \cdot x$ has a unique solution. However any number x solves the last equation, and consequently $0 \div 0$ cannot be defined. Suppose $0 \div 0 = 1$. Because $0 = 0 \cdot 2$, if we divide both sides of the equation by 0, then $1 = 1 \cdot 2$ or $1 = 2$. Thus, $0 \div 0 = 1$ leads to a contradiction, and consequently it cannot be defined as 1.

15. (a) This is true as long as $b \neq 0$. By definition of division, $(a \cdot b) \div b = x$ if and only if $ab = xb$ has a unique solution. If $b \neq 0$, the unique solution is ab.
    (b) When $b = 0$ the equation $ab = xb$ does not have a unique solution since any value of x will satisfy it. Hence the student cannot substitute $b = 0$.

16. In general, $a \div (b - c) \neq (a \div b) - (a \div c)$. For example, $100 \div (25-5) \neq (100 \div 25) - (100 \div 5)$. In fact the right-hand side is $4 - 20$, which is not defined in the set of whole numbers. However, the right distributive property of division over subtraction does hold provided each expression is defined in the set of whole numbers; that is
    $(b - c) \div a = (b \div a) - (c \div a)$.

17. The student probably has in mind the fact that if $a \in W$, $a - 0 = a$. It should be pointed out that 0 would be the identity for subtraction if $0 - a = a$ was also true. Since $0 - a$ is not defined in the set of whole numbers, $0 - a \neq a$ and therefore 0 is not the identity for subtraction.

18. Any number can be represented by a directed arrow of a given length. In this case, the directed arrow represents 3 units. Any arrow 3 units in length can be used to represent 3, regardless of its starting point.

19. Let $A = \{1, 2, 3\}$ and $B = \{4, 5, 6\}$. The set $\{(1, 4), (2, 5), (3, 6)\}$ is a function from A to B and it is a subset of $A \times B$. However not every subset of $A \times B$ is a function from A to B. For example
    $\{(1, 4), (1, 5), (2, 5), (3, 6)\}$ is a subset of $A \times B$ but it is not a function because two different ordered pairs with the same first component are in the set. In general a function from A to B is a subset of $A \times B$ but not every subset of $A \times B$ is a function from A to B.

20. The student is wrong. The ordered pair (x, y) is considered a single input. If x and y are in N then (x, y) is an element in $N \times N$ and hence the domain of the function is $N \times N$.

Chapter 3

1. (a) The first equation is true because $39 + 41 = 39 + (1 + 40) = (39 + 1) + 40 = 40 + 40$. Now, $39 \cdot 41 = (40 - 1)(40 + 1) = (40 - 1) 40 + (40 - 1)1 = 40^2 - 40 + 40 - 1$ $= 40^2 - 1$, and $40^2 - 1 \neq 40^2$.
   (b) Yes, this pattern continue because the numbers being considered are in the form $(a - 1)(a + 1)$ which is equal to $a^2 - 1$.

Chapter 3 (cont.)

2. Answers vary, for example, the rounding strategy may not always be the easiest or fastest way to do an estimation. For example, the clustering strategy is much faster if all the numbers are roughly grouped around a particular value. Depending upon the values of the numbers, strategies like using compatible numbers make the estimation process much easier. Front-end estimation is quick and easy and in many cases can lead to a better estimate.

3. Answers vary, for example, in base two we have two numerals, in base five we have five numerals, and in base ten we have ten numerals so what would it mean to have a negative number of numerals?

4. Answers vary, for example, you might first ask if the answer is reasonable, that is, since $3 \cdot 45$ is only 135 the answer of 45 is off. Also, $3 \cdot 400 = 1200$ so the answer must be greater than 400 since there are at least 400 set of three in 1215. There are five more threes in 15 so the final answer must be $400 + 5 = 405$. So we see that somehow we are missing the placeholder of 0 in the quotient. Next we might work the problem using repeated subtraction and scaffolding to show that we are really taking away 400 sets of three and not 40. In the student's work the placeholder of 0 is missing.

$$
\begin{array}{r}
405 \\
5 \\
400 \\
\hline
3 \overline{)1215} \\
-1200 \\
\hline
15 \\
-15 \\
\hline
0
\end{array}
$$

5. In a place value system, there are ten numerals and in the Roman system this does not happen. A base-ten system use place value and face value. The Roman system uses the additive, subtractive and multiplicative properties and does not use place value.

6. Evidently the student does not understand the process of long division. The repeated subtraction method should help in understanding the mistake.

$$
\begin{array}{r}
6 \overline{)36} \\
-6 \quad | \; 1 \text{ six} \\
\hline
30 \\
-30 \quad | \; 5 \text{ sixes} \\
\hline
6 \text{ sixes}
\end{array}
$$

Instead of adding 1 and 5, the student wrote 15.

7. It is correct. However, Romans usually reserved the bar for numbers greater than 4000. Because M is a special symbol for 1000, it is preferable to write MI for 1001 rather than $\overline{\text{II}}$.

Chapter 3 (cont.)

8. To show the parent a current view about the use of manipulatives in the classroom, the NCTM *Principles and Standards* can be used to show a professional opinion about their use. Possibly the parent went to school in an era when the use of counting on fingers was discouraged.

9. We see on the calculator that 592 divided by 36 is $16.\overline{4}$. This tells us there are 16 sets of 36 in 592 with some left over. To determine how many are left over we could multiply $16 \cdot 36 = 576$ and then subtract 576 from 592 to obtain a remainder of 16. Another way to think about it is to use the Division Algorithm, that is, $a = bq + r$. Solving for r we have $r = a - bq = 596 - 36 \cdot 16 = 16$.

Chapter 4

1. The algorithm is correct, and the student should be congratulated for finding it. One way to encourage such creative behavior is to name and refer to the procedure after the student, who invented it, for example, "David's subtraction method." In fourth grade the technique can be explained by using a money model. Suppose you have $4 in one checking account and $80 in another, for a total of $84. You spent $27 by withdrawing $7 from the first account and $20 from the second. The first checking account is overdrawn by $3; that is, the balance is $^-\$3$. The balance is the second account is $60. After transferring $3 from the second account to the first, the balance in the first account is $0 and in the second $57; that is, the total balance is $57.

2. The student is correct that a debt of $5 is greater than a debt of $2. However, what this means is that on a number line $^-5$ is farther to the left than is $^-2$. The fact that $^-5$ is farther to the left than $^-2$ on a number line implies that $^-5 < ^-2$.

3. The student does not complete the argument in detail. Indeed $a - b = a + ^-b$. However, $b - a = b + ^-a$. In general, $a + ^-b \neq b + ^-a$. For example, $5 + ^-2 \neq 2 + ^-5$.

4. The student does not fully understand the order of operations. The teacher should emphasize that in order to avoid ambiguity, mathematicians agree that multiplication is performed before addition or subtraction. A few simpler examples like $10 - 2 \cdot 3$ should be helpful.

5. The procedure can be justified as follows. Since for all integers c, $^-c = (^-1)c$, the effect of performing the opposite of an algebraic expression is the same as multiplying the expression by $^-1$. However, in the expression $x - (2x - 3)$, the "$-$" is used to denote subtraction, not simply finding the opposite. If the expression is first rewritten as $x + ^-(2x + ^-3)$, then it is the case that $^-(2x + ^-3) = ^-1(2x + ^-3)$, or $^-2x + 3$. Now the expression can be rewritten as $x + ^-2x + 3$, which a student might obtain from the father's rule.

Chapter 4 (cont.)

6. The picture is supposed to illustrate the fact that an integer and its opposite are mirror images of each other. Because a could be negative, the picture is correct. For example, possible values for a and ^-a are $a = {^-}1$, $^-a = 1$ and $a = {^-}7$, $^-a = 7$. At this point, the teacher could remind the students that the "–" sign in ^-a *does* not mean that ^-a is negative. If a is positive, ^-a is negative, but if a is negative, ^-a is positive.

7. For most students at this level numerical examples or a number line argument should suffice. Some may appreciate the following rigorous argument: suppose $a \le 0$ and $b \le 0$, then $a + b \le 0$ and hence $|a + b| = {^-}(a + b)$ and therefore $a + b = {^-}|a + b|$. If $a \ge 0$ and $b \le 0$, then $|b| = -b$ and $|a| = a$. Hence, $a + b = |a| + {^-}|b| = |a| - |b|$. The arguments in the other two cases are similar.

8. Yes if $a \ne 0$. The students' conclusion is that $a \mid 0$ and this is true because if $a \ne 0$ the equation $a \cdot k = 0$ has a unique solution $k = 0$.

9. The student is generalizing the statement "if $d \mid a$ and $d \mid b$, then $d \mid (a + b)$" to the corresponding statement for "does not divide." (Generalizations have to be checked carefully.) The statement the student wrote is false; for example, $3 \nmid 7$ and $3 \nmid 2$, but $3 \mid (7 + 2)$.

10. It has been shown that any four-digit number n can be written in the form $n = a \cdot 10^3 + b \cdot 10^2 + c \cdot 10 + d = (a \cdot 999 + b \cdot 99 + c \cdot 9) + (a + b + c + d)$. The test for divisibility by some number g will depend on the sum of the digits $a + b + c + d$ if, and only if, $g \mid (a \cdot 999 + b \cdot 99 + c \cdot 9)$ regardless of the values of a, b, and c. Since the only numbers greater than 1 that divide 9, 99, and 999 are 3 and 9, the test for divisibility by dividing the sum of the digits by the number works only for 3 and 9. A similar argument works for any n-digit number.

11. The student is wrong. For example, 1029 is divisible by 7, but neither 29 nor 10 is divisible by 7. However, it is true that a number with an even number of digits is divisible by 7 if each of the numbers formed by pairing the digits into groups of two is divisible by 7. The proof for any six-digit number follows. (The proof for any number with an even number of digits is similar.) Let $a \cdot 10^5 + b \cdot 10^4 + c \cdot 10^3 + d \cdot 10^2 + e \cdot 10 + f$ be any six-digit number such that 7 divides each of the two-digit numbers $a \cdot 10 + b$, $c \cdot 10 + d$, and
$e \cdot 10 + f$. The number, n, can be written as follows:
$n = a \cdot 10^5 + b \cdot 10^4 + c \cdot 10^3 + d \cdot 10^2 + e + 10 + f$
$\quad = (a \cdot 10 + b)10^4 + (c \cdot 10 + d)10^2 + (e \cdot 10 + f)$.
Since 7 divides $(e \cdot 10 + f)$, $(c \cdot 10 + d)$, and $(a \cdot 10 + b)$, it follows from the basic properties of divisibility that $7 \mid [(a \cdot 10 + b)10^4 + (c \cdot 10 + d)10^2 + (e \cdot 10 + f)]$.

12. The statement that there are infinitely many primes is true but it does not follow from the student's argument. We can say that unlike when finding successive counting numbers, where it is possible to produce the next number by adding one, there is no known way to produce the next prime from a given prime number.

Chapter 4 (cont.)

13. It is true that a number is divisible by 21 if, and only if, it is divisible by 3 and by 7. However, the general statement is false. For example, 12 is divisible by 4 and by 6 but not by $4 \cdot 6$ or 24. One part of the statement is true, that is, "if a number is divisible by $a \cdot b$, then it is divisible by a and b." The statement "if a number is divisible by a and by b, it is divisible by ab" it is true if a and b are relatively prime. To see why this is true, suppose GCD $(a, b) = 1$ and m is an integer such that $a \mid m$ and $b \mid m$. Since $a \mid m$, $m = ka$ for some integer k. Now $b \mid m$ implies that $b \mid ka$ for some integer k. Since a and b are relatively prime, it follows from the Fundamental Theorem of Arithmetic and the fact that $b \mid ka$ that $b \mid k$ (why?), and therefore $k = jb$, for some integer j. Substituting $k = jb$ in $m = ka$, we obtain $m = jba$, and consequently $ab \mid m$.

14. The student is partially correct. If a and b are distinct natural numbers, then the student is correct. By definition, $a \leq \text{LCM}(a, b)$; $b \leq \text{LCM}(a, b)$. Also $\text{GCD}(a, b) \leq a$ and $\text{GCD}(a, b) \leq b$. Hence, $\text{GCD}(a,b) \leq \text{LCM}(a, b)$. However, the equality holds if $a = b$.

15. $x = 3k, y = 4k, z = 5k$ satisfies the equation for any integer k. Hence the student is right.

16. The number 1 is not a prime because it does not have exactly two divisors; it has only one.

17. In finding the least common denominator of fractions, one must find the LCM of the denominators. Thus the LCM of a set of denominators is the least common denominator.

Chapter 5

1. 0/6 is not in simplest form. A fraction a/b is in simplest form if and only if $\text{GCD}(a,b)=1$; however $\text{GCD}(0,6) = 6$. The simplest form of 0/6 is 0/1, or 0.

2. Let the number be a. One half of a is $(1/2)(a) = a/2$. Dividing a by 1/2 yields $2a$. Consequently the student is incorrect.

3. The first student's approach is correct. What the second student has done is to treat the problem as if it had been $(1/5)(5/3)=1/3$, when in reality, the problem is 15/53. Writing the problem as $(10 + 5)/(50 + 3)$ may help.

4. No. Because $2/3 - 1/2 = 1/6$ and $3/4 - 2/3 = 1/12$, there is no fixed number that can be added to each term in order to obtain the next term.

5. Yes. The student is correct. Suppose that the fractions are positive and $a/b < c/d$. This inequality is equivalent to $ad < bc$. The student claims that $a/b < (a + c)/(b + d) < c/d$. This is equivalent to $a(b + d) < b(a + c)$ and $(a + c)d < c(b + d)$. However, each of the last inequalities is equivalent to $ad < bc$.

6. Yes, the student is correct. Let $a/b = c/d = r$. Then $a = br, c = dr$, and therefore $(a + c)/(b + d) = (br + dr)/(b + d) = r(b + d)/(b + d) = r = a/b = c/d$.

Chapter 5 (cont.)

7. The student is generalizing the distributive property of multiplication over addition to the distributive property of multiplication over multiplication. The latter does not hold.

8. The student is wrong unless $n = 0$ or $p = m$.

9. The student was probably thinking that more pieces meant more pizza. A pizza (or circle) could be cut into 6 pieces, then each piece could be cut into 2 pieces. This shows the amount of pizza did not change from these last cuts, only the number of pieces changed.

10. The student is incorrect but has an idea about finding the limit of $(a + x)/(b + x)$ when x is very large. The limit of that expression as x becomes very large is 1.

11. The teacher was right. Nat obtained the correct answer by using an incorrect method because in general $a + b(x + c) \neq (a + b)(x + c)$. Some advanced students could be encouraged to find other equations for which a similar mistake will produce a correct answer. This will happen if the equations $a + b(x + c) = x + d$ and $(a + b)(x + c) = x + d$ have the same solution. This can be shown to happen if and only if $d = a + b + c - 1$. Consequently, a, b, and c can be chosen at will but d is determined by the above equation.

12. The student is incorrect. An improper fraction is defined in terms of positive numerators and denominators.

13. The student is incorrect. A pattern is being followed that is untrue.

Chapter 6

1. 0.36 can be written as 36/100 and 0.9 can be written as 9/10. Comparing the numerators of the fractions will not determine which fraction is greater because the denominators are different. To compare the fractions, they need to have the same denominator. Because $0.9 = 0.90 = 90/100$ and 90 is greater than 36, $0.9 > 0.36.5$.

2. Scientific notation is typically used for very large numbers or very small numbers (numbers close to 0). In scientific notation, a number N is written in the form $N = A \cdot 10^n$ where $1 \leq A < 10$. Thus, negative numbers are not considered in this definition. If this notation is to be used with negative numbers, we can work with the number as if it were a positive number and then annex a negative sign at the end, for example, $-2,390,000$ could be written as $-2.39 \cdot 10^6$.

3. In the second method, the student did not use the distributive property correctly. Notice that $(8 + 1/2) (6 + 1/2) = (8 + 1/2)6 + (8 + 1/2)(1/2)$. Because $(8 + 1/2)6 = 8 \cdot 6 + (1/2) \cdot 6 = 48 + 3$, the 3 is missing in the student's example. Adding 3 to the student's answer results in the correct answer of 55 1/4.

4. $3\frac{1}{4}\% = 3\% + \frac{1}{4}\% = 3/100 + (\frac{1}{4})/100 = 0.03 + 0.0025 = 0.0325$. Knowing that $1/4 = 0.25$, the student incorrectly wrote $1/4\% = 0.25$.

Chapter 6 (cont.)

5. It is possible to mark up the price of a product 150%. For example, if a product sells for $10, then a 150% markup is 1.5($10) = $15. Thus, the product would sell for $25.

6. Let s denote the amount of salary. After $p\%$ increase, the new salary is $s(1 + p/100)$. When this amount is decreased by $q\%$, the result is $s(1 + p/100)(1 - q/100)$. Similarly if the initial salary is first decreased by $q\%$ and then the new amount is raised by $p\%$, the final salary is $s(1 - q/100)(1 + p/100)$. Because the two expressions are equal, the student is right.

7. By definition $p\% = p/100$, where p is any real number. Hence $0.01\% = 0.01/100$. Because $0.01/100 \neq 0.01$, the student is wrong.

8. It is evident what happens when 0.5 is raised to large powers. Because $\left(\frac{1}{2}\right)^{10} = \frac{1}{1024}$ and

   $$\frac{1}{2^{20}} = \left[\left(\frac{1}{2}\right)^{10}\right]^2 = \frac{1}{1,048,576},$$ it is clear that $\frac{1}{2}$ raised to a positive integer, gets quickly

   close to 0. In fact any number between 0 and 1 when raised to a sufficiently large exponent will get as close to 0 as we wish. At the level of this course it may be sufficient to use a calculator to see what happens when 0.999 is raised to large powers. Using the $\boxed{x^2}$ key repeatedly we get: 0.9841194, 0.9684911, 0.937975, 0.879797, 0.7740428, .5991423, 0.3589715, ... which are the approximate values of 0.999^2, 0.999^4, 0.999^8, 0.999^{16}, ..., 0.999^{1024}. We see that the tenth term in the sequence is less than 0.5 and hence further squaring should quickly result in numbers closer and closer to 0.

9. (a) The calculator does not carry the decimals out far enough to compare the two numbers.

   (b) $\dfrac{9444}{9445} - \dfrac{9443}{9444} > 0,$

   $\dfrac{9444^2 - 9443 \cdot 9445}{9444 \cdot 9445} > 0$

   The last inequality is true if and only if the numerator of the fraction is positive. Using a calculator we find that $9444^2 - 9443 \cdot 9445 = 1$ and hence that

   $$\frac{9444}{9445} > \frac{9443}{9444}$$

   It is possible to determine which fraction is greater with fewer calculations as follows.

   $$\frac{9443}{9444} = \frac{9444 - 1}{9444} = 1 - \frac{1}{9444} \text{ and } \frac{9444}{9445} = \frac{9445 - 1}{9445} = 1 - \frac{1}{9445}.$$

   Because $\dfrac{1}{9445} < \dfrac{1}{9444}, \dfrac{-1}{9445} > \dfrac{-1}{9444}$ and hence, $1 - \dfrac{1}{9445} > 1 - \dfrac{1}{9444}.$

Chapter 6 (cont.)

Yet another approach is to multiply each decimal equivalent by 10. Because $\frac{9444}{9445} \cdot 10$ is displayed as 9.998412 and $\frac{9443}{9444} \cdot 10$ as 9.89411, the first fraction is the greater one. However this approach will not work to show that $\frac{94444}{94445} > \frac{94443}{94444}$.

10. The principal square root of 25, written $\sqrt{25}$, is defined to be the nonnegative number whose square is 25. Consequently, $\sqrt{25} = 5$.

11. The principal square root of a^2 is always nonnegative. Hence, $\sqrt{a^2} = a$ if $a > 0$. If $a < 0$, then $-a$ is positive, and hence $\sqrt{a^2} = -a$. For example, if $a = -5$, then $\sqrt{(-5)^2} = {}^-(-5) = 5$. Consequently the student is wrong.

12. All properties of integral exponents do not automatically extend to rational exponents. The corresponding properties for rational exponents have to be justified. The property $\left(a^m\right)^n = a^{mn}$ is true when a is nonnegative and m and n are rational numbers. For $a < 0$, m an even integer and $n = 1/m$, the property is false. For example, $\left((-5)^2\right)^{1/2} \neq -5$.

13. Most likely, the student thinks that $-x$ is a negative number. This is wrong. Depending upon the value of x, $-x$ can be positive, negative, or 0. If $x < 0$, then $-x > 0$. In fact, $x = -9$ is the solution of the given equation.

14. Because the formula for compound interest is $A = P(1 + r)^n$ and $P = \$d$ and $r = 1$, then we have $A = d(1 + 1)^n = d \cdot 2^n$. Thus, the student is correct.

Chapter 7

1. Each toss of a fair coin is independent of the previous one. Hence the probability of a tail on each toss is $\frac{1}{2}$ regardless of how many tails appeared in previous tosses.

2. If the four areas corresponding to the colors were equal in size, the events of the spinner landing on each of the colors would be equally likely, and the student would be correct. However, since the four areas are different in size, the events are not equally likely, and the student is wrong.

3. Tossing three heads on the first three tosses of a coin does not imply the coin is unfair. Only when a fair coin is tossed a much greater number of times can we expect to get approximately equal numbers of tails and heads. The probability of three heads in three tosses is $\frac{1}{8}$.

Chapter 7 (cont.)

4. The student is wrong. The sample space for this event is not $\{HH, HT, TT\}$, but rather $\{HH, HT, TH, TT\}$. Consequently the probability of HH is $\frac{1}{4}$.

5. The student is not correct. The confusion probably lies in the fact that the student thinks that probabilities are additive. The student does not understand the Multiplication Rule for Probabilities. A tree diagram for the experiment could possibly help. A partial tree diagram is given below:

$$\xrightarrow{\frac{1}{6}} 5 \xrightarrow{\frac{1}{6}} 5$$

Thus $P(5,5) = \frac{1}{6} \cdot \frac{1}{6} = \frac{1}{36}$

6. For an experiment with sample space S with equally likely outcomes, the probability of an event A is given by $P(A) = \frac{n(A)}{n(S)}$. Because an event A must be a subset of S, the smallest that $n(A)$ could be is 0. This occurs when $A = \varnothing$. Because $n(S)$ is never negative and $n(A)$ is never negative, then the $P(A)$ can never be negative.

7. The probability of an event is a ratio and does not necessarily reflect the number of elements in the event or in the sample space. For example, if $n(S) = 20$ and $n(A) = 12$, then $P(A) = \frac{12}{20}$ which could also be reported as $P(A) = \frac{3}{5}$.

8. Suppose the odds in favor of winning a game are 1:2. Even when the outcomes are equally likely it does not mean that out of every 3 games the player will win 1 game. It only means that if a large number of games are played, the ratio between the number of wins and the number of losses is close to $\frac{1}{2}$. However, the answer is correct because the solution of the equation $\frac{P(W)}{1 - P(W)} = \frac{a}{b}$ is $\frac{a}{a+b}$.

9. The student is confused about choosing four objects none at a time. In any set of choices, there is always the option of choosing nothing, and there is one way to choose nothing. Therefore, we say $_4P_0 = 1$.

10. We define 0! as 1 because it fits the formula for combinations. It is also consistent with the rest of mathematics. To define 1/0 as 1 would cause many inconsistencies. If 1/0 = 1 and 1/1 = 1, then 1/0 = 1/1 which should imply that 0 = 1. This is not true.

Chapter 7 (cont.)

11. For all multistage experiments, the probability of the outcome along any path in a tree diagram is equal to the product of the probabilities along the path. The sum of the probabilities on all the branches from any point is always 1 and the sum of the probabilities for all the possible outcomes is always 1. The probability of an event is the sum of the probabilities of the elements in the event.

Chapter 8

1. The new mean is $\dfrac{9(10,000) + 20,000}{10} = 11,000$. Consequently the new mean has increased by \$1000. The median and mode may be changed in special cases, for example, if the scores were 2000, 8000, 8000, 8000, 9000, 10,000, 12,000, 12,000, 13,000, and 18,000, then the median and mode change.

2. A first discussion might include asking what the student means by the "best average." If the student is thinking of choosing from the mean, median, or mode, then we need to discuss which is the most appropriate. The mode is used if it is desirable to know which value occurs most often in the distribution. For example, if a store wants to know which size pants is most frequently sold, the mode is the most appropriate average to use.

3. The student is not correct. The stem and leaf plot is very useful when trying to organize information that will later be used to make a bar graph or a frequency polygon. It is not the most useful plot when trying to depict information that will be organized into a circle graph for example.

4. Since the median is 90, at least half of the class had grades of 90 or more. Since Tom scored 80, he did not do better than half of the class.

5. A graph displays the data in a way that is possible to see at a glance how parts of the data compare to each other. One of the disadvantages of graphical representation is that it is not always possible to obtain accurate readings from graphs.

6. In a grouped frequency table, the precise value of the raw data is not displayed, and hence it is impossible to conclude from the table which value occurs most often. Consequently it is impossible to find the exact mode from the information given in a grouped frequency table. In this situation the mode is usually given as a class interval.

7. If the mean is less than the median, then one can be certain that there were more scores above the mean than below it. The low scores tend to be further from the mean than the high scores.

8. No, it is not possible to have a standard deviation of –5. By definition, the standard deviation is the positive square root of the variance.

9. Mel did not really miss the cut-off by a single point. She would have had to increase her score on each of the 10 tests by a single point to reach an average of 90 or increase her total score for the 10 tests by 10 points to reach an average of 90.

Chapter 8 (cont.)

10. Bar graphs are typically used to display data that is not continuous, for example, the number of students in each sixth grade class at Washington School. Bar graphs are used when data falls into distinct categories and we want to compare the totals. The line graph is more appropriate when we want to emphasize trends in data that change continuously over time.

11. The student is not correct. The data could consist of many data points, all of which have the same numerical value. In that case, the mean, median, and all data points have the same value.

12. The answer is probably "Yes." A manufacturer should be able to ensure with some degree of accuracy that his product is the "same" all the time. In order to do that, then tools should be calibrated with a small standard deviation.

13. An average deviation is sometimes used, but most people use the standard deviation. To find the average deviation, one would start the process like finding the standard deviation by finding the difference of a data value and the mean. One would then sum all the differences and find their mean. The average deviation may be misleading; you can have an average deviation of 0 when the standard deviation is nowhere close to 0.

Chapter 9

1. From the Denseness Property, we know that for any two real numbers, there is a real number between them. Because points of a line and the set of real numbers can be put in a one-to-one correspondence, we can always find a point between any two points. Since this is true for any two points, we see that there are an infinite number of points in a segment.

2. The distinct lines are parallel if they do not intersect and are contained in a single plane. Lines that do not intersect and are not contained in any single plane are called skew lines.

3. The measure of an angle has nothing to do with the fact that rays cannot be measured. The measure of an angle in degrees is based on constructing a circle with center at the vertex of the angle and dividing the circle into 360 congruent parts. The number of parts in the arc that the angle intercepts is the measure of the given angle in degrees. The number of parts in the intercepted arc is the same regardless of the size of the circle (or protractor).

4. Extending the rays does not change the angle measure.

5. A regular polygon is a polygon in which all the angles are congruent and all the sides are congruent. In general neither condition implies the other, and hence neither is sufficient to describe a regular polygon. For example, a rhombus that is not a square has all sides congruent, but all its angles are not congruent. A rectangle that is not a square has all its angles congruent, but not all its sides congruent. Neither a rhombus nor a rectangle is a regular polygon unless they are squares.

Chapter 9 (cont.)

6. Let *n* be the number of sides of a regular polygon, all of whose angles measure 90 degrees. The sum of the measures of all the interior angles is $n \cdot 90 = (n - 2)\, 180$. This equation has the solution $n = 4$. Thus the polygon must have 4 sides, and therefore it is necessarily a square.

7. If two parallel lines are defined as lines that are in the same plane and have no points in common, then two identical lines cannot be parallel, because they have infinitely many points in common. It is possible to define two identical lines as parallel or nonparallel. Some books define it one way; other books the other way.

8. Cut the cylinder open along any line perpendicular to the base. The shortest path between *A* and *B* is the segment connecting *A* and *B*. Now fold the rectangle back into the cylinder; the path will appear on the cylinder.

9. Since an angle is a set of points determined by two rays with the same endpoint, to say that two angles are equal implies that the two sets of points determining the angles are equal. The only way this can happen is if the two angles are actually the same angle. To say that two angles are congruent is to say that the angles have the same size or measure.

10. The student is incorrect. While the degree is the basic unit of angle measure, it can be further subdivided. This in itself would prove that the student is incorrect. However, many geometry books also consider a Protractor Postulate which puts all the rays in a half-line emanating from a point in a one-to-one correspondence with the real numbers greater than or equal to 0 and less than 180. This would allow infinitely many rays emanating from one point.

11. A square is a particular kind of rectangle in which all sides have equal measures. All squares are rectangles.

12. To be regular, all sides must be congruent but also all angles must be congruent. All angles are not congruent unless the rhombus is a square.

13. One consideration for a geometry to be considered "Euclidean" is if in a plane and through a given point not on a given line, there is exactly one line parallel to the given line. The geometry of a globe is an example of a non-Euclidean geometry.

14. Geometry is worthy of study for many reasons. From a purely mathematical standpoint, the geometry is a beautiful mathematical structure that can start with axioms, postulates, and definitions and can be built with theorems and proofs. Another reason to study different geometries is their usefulness in describing the world in which we live.

Chapter 10

1. The symbol ≅ used only for congruent parts. Because *AB* and *CD* designate length of segments and not the segments themselves, it is not true that $AB \cong CD$. Notice that if segments are congruent, then they are of the same length; hence it is correct to write $AB = CD$.

Chapter 10 (cont.)

2. Some of the constructions that cannot be done using a compass and straightedge are angle trisection, duplication of a cube, and squaring the circle. Given any angle, it is impossible with only a compass and straightedge to find two rays which divide the angle into three congruent angles. Some angles, but not all, can be trisected with straightedge and compass. For example, a right angle can be trisected. The duplication of a cube involves constructing the edge of a cube whose volume is twice the volume of a given cube. Squaring a circle involves constructing a square which has the same area as a given circle. For over 2000 years mathematicians tried to perform these three constructions. In the nineteenth century it was finally proved that these constructions cannot be done with straightedge and compass alone. A clear exposition of these proofs can be found in the book by Courant and Robbins, *What Is Mathematics?* (London: Oxford University Press, 1941 and 1969, pp. 117-140).

3. Perhaps the "best" definition relies on transformational geometry discussed in Chapter 12. Two figures can be defined to be congruent if and only if one figure can be mapped onto the other by successively applying translation, reflection, rotation, or glide reflection. For similarity add a size transformation.

4. For a detailed discussion of the trisection problem, see *The Trisection Problem*, by Robert Yates (Washington, D. C.: NCTM Publications, 1971).

5. The student is wrong. $\angle 1 \cong \angle 2$ implies that $\overline{AD}$ and $\overline{BC}$ are parallel, but does not imply that the other two sides are parallel.

6. This is false. Consider, for example, a rectangle which is not a square. The polygon resulting from connecting the midpoints of the sides of the rectangle is a rhombus with no right angles. Such a rhombus is not similar to the rectangle.

7. The symbol $=$ is used for identical objects. Two triangles are equal if they represent the same set of points. Congruent triangles are not necessarily identical because their positions may be different.

8. The student is wrong. The student is forgetting that when we say $\triangle ABC$ is congruent to $\triangle BCA$, this means that there is a one-to-one correspondence set up among the vertices so that corresponding sides are congruent. If $\triangle ABC$ is congruent to $\triangle BCA$, then $\overline{AB} \cong \overline{BC}$, $\overline{AC} \cong \overline{BA}$, and $\overline{BC} \cong \overline{CA}$. This is not true in a general triangle.

9. The answer is no. For example a square and a rectangle do not have to be congruent though both have all 90° angles.

10. The student is correct. All *n*-gons for the same *n* have the same shape.

11. The student is correct. All circles have the same shape.

Chapter 10 (cont.)

12. The slope of a vertical line is undefined because division by 0 is impossible (also see the answer to Now Try This 10-11(b)). When a line is closer and closer to being a vertical line, the slope is getting bigger and bigger. One way to see this is to take two points whose y coordinates differ by 1. The corresponding x coordinates of the points will be close to each other and hence their difference will be close to 0. The slope resulting from dividing 1 by a very small number will be very large.

13. The student is correct but more explanation would be helpful. The student does not show why the contradiction implies that the lines are parallel. A possible explanation might be as follows: The lines will be parallel if they do not intersect, that is, if the system of equations has no solution. If the equations had a common solution, we would get $3x + 5 = 3x + 4$. But this implies that $5 = 4$ which is a contradiction. Hence, the assumption that there is a common solution is wrong and the lines do not intersect.

Chapter 11

1. The units have to be the same because volume is measured in cubic units. A cubic unit is the volume of a cube having all its dimensions measured in the same units.

2. Yes, the same type of relationship does hold. For a proof and discussion, see G. Polya, *Mathematics and Plausible Reasoning*, Vol. 1 (Princeton, N.J.: Princeton University Press, 1954, pp. 15-17).

3. No. An angle is a union of two rays. The student probably means the area of the interior of an angle. However, because the interior of an angle occupies an infinite part of a plane, it does not have a measurable area.

4. The area of the interior of any simple closed curve can be described as the sum of the areas of the finitely many nonoverlapping parts into which it can be divided. In the student's case, the square is divided into <u>infinitely</u> many parts, and hence the above property does not apply.

5. Consider a cube with side 6 cm. The volume is 216 cm^3 and its surface area is 216 cm^2.

6. The metric system is much simpler than the English system of measurement. For example, converting from one unit to another within the metric system requires only multiplication or division by a power of 10. Almost all the countries in the world are using the metric system. In order for the United States to be able to trade effectively with other countries, it is essential that it use the same system as everybody else.

Chapter 11 (cont.)

7. Using the student's reasoning, in a right isosceles triangle, the side opposite the 90° angle should be twice as long as the side opposite the 45° angle. We know that the hypotenuse, c, is $\sqrt{2}$ times the length of a leg.

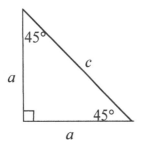

8. The given box has a volume of 125 cm³ and not 5 cm³. The student most likely thinks of 5 cm³ means (5 cm)³.

9. We use square centimeters or square inches to indicate the area of a square 1 cm or 1 in. on a side. However, we cannot have a square with 1 *are* or 1 *hectare* on a side because *are* and *hectare* are not linear measures. The area of a square 10 m on a side is 1 a, and 1 ha is the area of a square 100 m on a side.

10. Many areas cannot be found by the use of formulas, but that does not keep the area from existing. The argument is analogous to saying electricity does not exist because it cannot be seen.

11. The argument is no different here than for the area of a circle. A circle has curves and its area is in square units. All area is in square units. With a cylinder it is easy to see the lateral surface area if the cylinder is cut along an edge and opened up. The area is the same as a rectangle that has width equal to the height of the cylinder and length equal to the circumference of the circular base. Because this rectangle has area in square units, it makes sense that the lateral surface area is in square units.

12. For each degree change in Celsius, there is a 9/5 degree change in Fahrenheit. When a person's temperature is 2 degrees above normal Celsius, it is (9/5) • 2 or 3.6 degrees above normal Fahrenheit. Therefore, being 2 degrees above normal Celsius is more serious than being 2 degrees above normal Fahrenheit.

13. The area of a garden does not depend on the perimeter of the garden. For example, a garden that is 2 m by 6 m has a perimeter of 16 m and an area of 12 m². A garden that is 4 m by 4 m also has a perimeter of 16 m but has an area of 16 m².

14. The volume of the original rectangular prism is given by $V_1 = \ell wh$. The volume of the new prism is $V_2 = (2\ell)(2w)(2h) = 2 \cdot 2 \cdot 3(\ell wh) = 12\ell wh = 12\,V_1$. Therefore, Andrea is correct.

Chapter 12

1. The answer is no. If you are given only a single point and its image, then either a translation, rotation, reflection, or glide reflection could be used. It takes three noncollinear points to determine the isometry.

2. Again, having only a segment and its image is not enough to determine the transformation. It requires three noncollinear points. For a further examination of this problem, see *Transformational Geometry*, by Richard Brown (Palo Alto, CA: Dale Seymour Publications, 1989).

3. A kite always has one line of symmetry. This line of symmetry contains one of the diagonals. It is the diagonal through the vertices of the angles of the kite that are not necessarily congruent.

4. The student is wrong. One counterexample is a right triangular prism whose bases are scalene triangles.

5. We do have a function that is sometimes called a point transformation. Since it is not a one-to-one mapping of the plane to the plane, it is not a true transformation. The student is correct.

6. Let the translation on the grid be a translation from A to B. Let C be the vertex of a right $\triangle ABC$ where $\overline{AC}$ is in the horizontal direction. Then the translation from A to B can be accomplished by a translation from A to C followed by a translation from C to B.

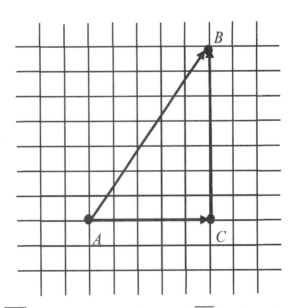

7. Construct $\triangle ACB$ so that $\overline{AC}$ is on one of the lines and $\overline{CB}$ on the other. The image of $\triangle ACB$ under a size transformation is a similar triangle. Hence an angle and its image are congruent. Consequently the image of $\angle ACB$ is a right angle and the image lines are perpendicular.

Chapter 12 (cont.)

8. Symmetries are used by architects and artists among others. As a design feature, symmetry is integral.

9. Many wheel covers on cars have symmetry for artistic reasons. The flashing of wheel covers typically makes a car look like it is going faster than it really may be. Few serve any functional purpose.

Chapter 1
Page 15   There are 232.

Page 35   35 moves. This can be solved using the strategy of examining simpler cases and looking for a pattern. If one person is on each side, 3 moves are necessary. If two people are on each side, 8 moves are necessary. With 3 people on each side, 15 moves are necessary. If n people are on each side, $(n+1)^2 - 1$ moves are required.

Chapter 2
Page 70   Because the town barber is a male, then he shaves himself. Because he shaves only those who do not shave them selves, he cannot shave himself. Consequently, the barber is not a male, but we know he is. This we have a paradox.

Page 91   Answers may vary. For example,

1	2	3
8	9	4
7	6	5

Page 118   The plan fails because we have not accounted for the eleventh man. The first and second men are in room 1, the third through tenth men are in rooms 2 through 9. Where is the eleventh man? He has not been mentioned. If the extra man in room 1 is put in room 10, then the eleventh man still has no room. Confusion results from the fact that by the time we read that the tenth man has been put into room 9, we think that the extra man in the first room is the eleventh man, when actually he is either the first or the second.

Chapter 3
Page 135   One box contains 2 nickels, one box contains 2 dimes, and one box contains a nickel and a dime. You would reach in the box labeled 15¢. It a nickel is drawn, the correct label for this box is 10¢. The 20¢ label would then be shifted to the box that was labeled 10¢, and then the 15¢ label would be placed on the remaining box. If a dime is drawn from the box labeled 15¢, then the 20¢ label would be placed on this box. Then the 10¢ label would be shifted to the box that was labeled 20¢, and the 15¢ label would be placed on the remaining box.

Page 142   The license plate number is 10968.

Page 156   a. $$\begin{array}{r} 570{,}140 \\ \times\quad 6 \\ \hline 3{,}420{,}840 \end{array}$$ b. $$\begin{array}{r} 38 \\ 38 \\ +\ 38 \\ \hline 114 \end{array}$$ or $$\begin{array}{r} 39 \\ 39 \\ +\ 39 \\ \hline 117 \end{array}$$

Chapter 4
Page 183 $123 - 45 - 67 + 89 = 100$.

Page 191   Answers may vary. $1 = 4^4/4^4$; $2 = (4 \cdot 4)/(4 + 4)$;
$3 = 4 - (4/4)^4$; $4 = [(4 - 4)/4] + 4$; $5 = 4 + 4^{(4 - 4)}$;
$6 = 4 + [(4 + 4)/4]$; $7 = (44/4) - 4$; $8 = [(4 + 4)/4] \cdot 4$;
$9 = 4 + 4\ 4/4$; $10 = (44 - 4)/4$

Page 194 0 because $(x - x) = 0$

Page 203   The part of the explanation that is incorrect is the division by $(e - a - d)$ which is equal to 0. Division by 0 is impossible.

Page 206   The number is 381-65-4729.

Page 223   If n is the width of the rectangle and m is the length of the rectangle, then the number of squares the diagonal crosses is $(n + m) - (GCD(n, m))$ or $(n + m) - 1$.

Page 240   There are no primes in this list.

Chapter 5
Page 267
Let $x =$ number of students

$$\frac{1}{2}x + \frac{1}{7}x + 20 = x$$
$$20 = \frac{5}{14}x$$
$$56 = x$$

Page 277   Observe that after crossing each bridge, the prince was left with half the bags he had previously minus one additional bag of gold. To determine the number he had prior to crossing the bridge, we can use the inverse operations; that is, add 1 and multiply by 2. The prince had one bag left after crossing the fourth bridge. He must have had two before he gave the guard the extra bag. Finally he must have had four bags before he gave the guard at the fourth bridge any bags. The entire procedure is summarized in the following table.

Bridge	Bags After Crossing	Bags Before Guard Given Extra	Bags Prior to Crossing
Fourth	1	2	4
Third	4	5	10
Second	10	11	22
First	22	23	46

Chapter 5 (cont.)
Page 281 No. The legacy is impossible because the fractions of cats to be shared do not add up to the whole units of cats.
$\frac{1}{2}x + \frac{1}{3}x + \frac{1}{9}x = \frac{17}{18}x$, but the sum should be $1x$, or $\frac{18}{18}x$.

Chapter 6
Page 330 Let C = amount of crust and P = amount of pie, x = percent of crust to be reduced. $C = 25\%$ of P, so $C(100 - x)/100 = (20/100)P$. Hence, $x = 20\%$.

Chapter 7
Page 378 These dice are truly remarkable in that no matter which die the other player chooses, you can always choose one that will beat it 3/2 of the time. Therefore, the strategy for playing this game is to go second and make your choice of die based on the information in the following table.

First Person's Choice	Second Person's Choice	Probability of Second Choice Winning
A	D	2/3
B	A	2/3
C	B	2/3
D	C	2/3

Page 403 (a) The probability of a successful flight with two engines is 0.9999.
(b) The probability of a successful flight with four engines is 0.99999603.

Chapter 8
Page 442 The mean speed for the total six-mile run is 6 divided by the total time it took to drive the 6 mi. The total time is the sum of the times spent on the first 3 mi., the next 1 1/2 mi. and the last 1 1/2 mi. On the first 3 mi., he averaged 140 mph. Thus, his time was 3/140 hr. Similarly, the times on the next two segments were 1.5/168 hr. and 1.5/210 hr. His total time was 3/140 + 1.5/168 + 0.5/210 = 0.0375 hr. Therefore, the mean speed was 6/0.375 = 60 mph.

Chapter 9
Page 492 360°

Page 506 See the article referenced by Hoffer to see the shape of the glass.

Page 513 The problem is impossible.

Chapter 10

Page 559 It can be shown that the fence post must be 6 ft high regardless of how far apart the flag poles are.

Page 566 When P is located at the midpoint of a side the length of the path is one half the perimeter of the triangle. In general, if P is not on a midpoint of a side, the length of the path is equal to the perimeter of the triangular base.

Chapter 11

p. 604 The tallest person on Earth could walk under the wire. Suppose the two concentric circles represent Earth and the lengthened wire. $\overline{OA}$ and $\overline{OB}$ are the radii of the respective circles and have lengths r and $r + x$. Because the circumference of the Earth plus 20 m equals the circumference of the lengthened wire, we have $2\pi r + 20 = 2\pi(r + x)$. Consequently, $x = 10/\pi$ or approximately 3.18 m.

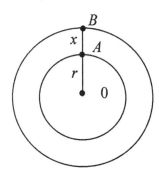

p. 621 1. 64 square units
2. 65 square units
3. Although the pieces look like they should fit together, they do not really fit. To see this, assume the pieces do fit. We then obtain the figure below.

Since $\triangle AEF \sim \triangle ACB$, we have $\dfrac{8}{13} = \dfrac{3}{5}$, which is a contradiction. This implies that pieces like those in the figure cannot fit together in order to form a triangle. In order for the pieces to fit together, the measure of $\overline{EF}$

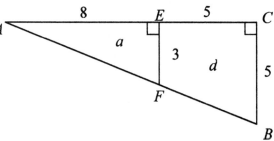

must be given as $\dfrac{8}{13} = \dfrac{EF}{5}$; hence $EF = \dfrac{40}{13} = 3\dfrac{1}{13}$. Since $3\dfrac{1}{13}$ is close to 3, the discrepancy is small that the pieces only appear to fit. Other pieces that appear to fit should be analyzed.

Chapter 11 (cont.)

p. 634   The room can be thought of as a box, which can be opened up so that A and C lie on the same plane. Then the shortest path is the line segment connecting A and C.

Thus $AC = \sqrt{2^2 + 6^2} = \sqrt{40} = 2\sqrt{10}$ m.

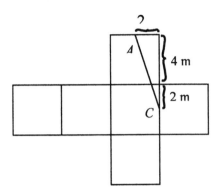

p. 644   The cone and the flattened region obtained by slitting the cone along a slant height are shown below.

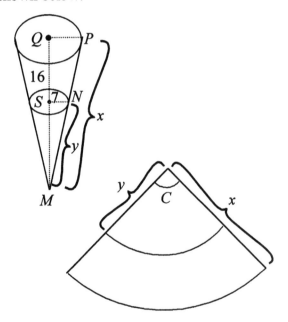

To construct the flattened ring we need to find x, y, and θ.

Because $\triangle MQP \sim \triangle MSN$ we have $\dfrac{16 + MS}{MS} = \dfrac{11}{7}$. Hence $MS = 28$ cm. In $\triangle MSN$ we have $28^2 + 7^2 = y^2$, or $y \doteq 28.86$. In $\triangle PQM : x^2 = 11^2 + 44^2$ or $x = 45.35$ cm. To find θ we roll the sector with radius y and central angle θ into the cone whose base is 7 cm and whose slant height is y. Hence $2\pi y \cdot \dfrac{\theta}{360} = 2\pi \cdot 7$, or $\theta =$

$\dfrac{7 \cdot 360}{28.86} \doteq 87° \ 19'$.

Chapter 12

Page 683   It will be as it now is. A translation is performed.

Page 695   Translate *B* towards *A* in the direction perpendicular to the banks of the river along the distance equal to the width of the river. Connect *A* with the image *B′*. The point *P* where $\overline{AB'}$ intersects the far bank is the point where the bridge should be built.

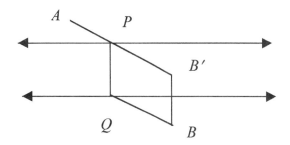

Page 4

1-1 (a) Answers vary, for example, the next three terms could be $\triangle$, $\triangle$, $\bigcirc$.

(b) If the rule is as given in (a), the pattern could be one circle, two triangles, one circle, two triangles, and so on in this manner.

Page 10

1-2 Because the 2nd term is 11, then $11 = a + d$. Because the 5th term is 23, then $23 = a + 4d$. Solving both equations for a and setting them equal, we have $11 - d = 23 - 4d$ which implies that
$d = 4$. To find the 100th term, we substitute in $a + (n - 1)d$ and the 100th term is
$7 + (100 - 1) 4 = 7 + 99 \cdot 4 = 403$.

Page 13

1-3 (a) After 10 hours, there are $2 \cdot 3^{10} = 118{,}098$ bacteria and after n hours there are $2 \cdot 3^n$ bacteria.

(b) After 10 hours, there are $2 + 10 \cdot 3 = 32$ bacteria and after n hours there are $2 + n \cdot 3$ bacteria. We can see after only 10 hours that geometric growth is much faster than arithmetic growth. In this case 118,098 vs. 32.

Page 22

1-4 The possibilities are given below.

ℓ	w	P
1	120	242
2	60	124
3	40	86
4	30	68
5	24	58
6	20	52
8	15	46
10	12	44

Therefore we see the least perimeter is obtained from the 10 x 12 (or 12 x 10) frame.

Page 24

1-5 No, she can seat $2 + 2 \cdot 25 = 52$ people this way. She can seat 20 people using a big square.

Page 26

1-6 Answers may vary. For example, because each person owes $13, Al could pay $4.25 to Betty and $4 to Carl; Dani could pay $7 to Carl; and everyone would be even.

Page 29

1-7 The building has 23 floors.

Page 62

2-1 (*a*) and (*b*) Number the swimming lanes 1, 2, 3, 4 and name the people *A*, *B*, *C*, *D*. Then we represent the correspondence:

$$
\begin{array}{ccc}
1 & \leftrightarrow & A \\
2 & \leftrightarrow & B \\
3 & \leftrightarrow & C \\
4 & \leftrightarrow & D
\end{array}
\qquad \text{as} \qquad
\begin{array}{cccc}
1 & 2 & 3 & 4 \\
A & B & C & D
\end{array}
$$

The 24 one-to-one correspondences are listed below:

1	2	3	4		1	2	3	4		1	2	3	4		1	2	3	4
A	B	C	D		B	A	C	D		C	A	B	D		D	A	B	C
A	B	D	C		B	A	D	C		C	A	D	B		D	A	C	B
A	C	B	D		B	C	A	D		C	B	A	D		D	B	A	C
A	C	D	B		B	C	D	A		D	B	D	A		D	B	C	A
A	D	B	C		B	D	A	C		C	D	A	B		D	C	A	B
A	D	C	B		B	D	C	A		C	D	B	A		D	C	B	A

(c)   We notice that: $24 = 4 \cdot 3 \cdot 2 = 4 \cdot 3 \cdot 2 \cdot 1$

We also notice that we had four choices for people to swim in lane 1. After making a choice, we see that we had three choices to swim in lane 2, leaving us with two choices for lane 3 and finally, one choice for lane 4. Extrapolating from this, we conjecture that there are

$$5 \cdot 4 \cdot 3 \cdot 2 \cdot 1 = 120$$

distinct one-to-one correspondences between a pair of five-element sets.

Page 64

2-2 If event M_1 can occur in m_1 ways, and after it has occurred, event M_2 can occur in m_2 ways, and after it has occurred, event M_3 can occur in m_3 ways, and so on where events $M_1, M_2, M_3,...$ can occur correspondingly in $m_1, m_2, m_3,...$ ways, then event M_1 followed by event M_2 followed by event $M_3, ...,$ followed by event M_n can occur in $m_1 \cdot m_2 \cdot m_3 \cdot ... \cdot m_n$ ways.

Page 64

2-3 No, two sets may be equivalent without being equal. To see this consider the following example:

$$
\begin{aligned}
A &= \{a, b, c\} \\
B &= \{1, 2, 3\}.
\end{aligned}
$$

Then:

$$
\begin{array}{c}
a \leftrightarrow 1 \\
b \leftrightarrow 2 \\
c \leftrightarrow 3
\end{array}
$$

is a one-to-one correspondence between *A* and *B*, and therefore $A \sim B$. However, $A \neq B$.

Page 67

2-4 (a)   Yes, by definition, $A \subseteq B$ means that every element of A is an element of B. Similarly, $A \subset B$ means that every element of A is an element of B but there exists an element in B which is not an element of A. Hence, if $A \subset B$, it is true that every element of A is in B. Consequently, $A \subseteq B$. Notice that if the more stringent condition $A \subset B$ is satisfied, then the weaker condition $A \subseteq B$ must also be satisfied.

(b)   No. To see this, consider the following counterexample:

$$A = \{a, b, c\}$$
$$B = \{a, b, c\}.$$

Then , $A \subseteq B$. Notice that $A \not\subset B$ since $A = B$.

Page 69

2-5 (a)   Assuming that a simple majority forms a winning coalition, we see that any subset consisting of three or more senators is a winning coalition. There are 16 such subsets. To see this, let $\{A,B,C,D,E\}$ be the set of five senators on the committee. Then the following are all possible winning coalitions:

$\{A, B, C\}$	$\{A, B, D\}$	$\{A, B, E\}$	$\{A, C, D\}$
$\{A, C, E\}$	$\{A, D,E\}$	$\{B, C, D\}$	$\{B, C, E\}$
$\{B, D,E\}$	$\{C, D, E\}$	$\{A, B, C, D\}$	$\{A, B, C, E\}$
$\{A, B, D, E\}$	$\{A, C, D, E\}$	$\{B, C, D, E\}$	$\{A, B, C, D, E\}$

(b)   From the list in part (a), we see that there are five subsets containing exactly four members. We also see that there are five senators on the committee. To understand why these numbers are the same, notice that creating a four-element subset is equivalent to deleting a single element from the total set. That is, we can give a one-to-one correspondence between the set of four-element subsets of $\{A,B,C,D,E\}$ and the set of senators by corresponding to each four-element subset the senator who is not in that subset as shown:

$$\{A, B, C, D\} \longleftrightarrow E$$
$$\{A, B, C, E\} \longleftrightarrow D$$
$$\{A, B, D, E\} \longleftrightarrow C$$
$$\{A, C, D, E\} \longleftrightarrow B$$
$$\{B, C, D, E\} \longleftrightarrow A$$

(c)   We can give a one-to-one correspondence between the three-element subsets and the two-element subsets of $\{A, B, C, D, E\}$ by matching each three-element subset with the unique two-element subset which contains the senators on the committee, but not in the subset. For example: $\{A, B, C\} \leftrightarrow \{D, E\}$.
From part (a), we know that there are exactly 10 three-element subsets of the committee, hence, there must be 10 two-element subsets of the committee.

Page 73

2-6 The formula is: $n(A \cup B) = n(A) + n(B) - n(A \cap B)$

To justify this formula, notice that in $n(A \cup B)$, the elements of $A \cap B$ are counted only once. In $n(A) + n(B)$, the elements of $A \cap B$ are counted twice; once in A and once in B. Thus, subtracting $n(A \cap B)$ from $n(A) + n(B)$ makes the number equal to $n(A \cup B)$.

For example: If $A = \{a, b, c\}$ and $B = \{c, d\}$ then $A \cup B = \{a, b, c, d\}$ and $n(A \cup B) = 4$. However, $n(A) + n(B) = 3 + 2 = 5$ since c is counted twice. Because $A \cap B = \{c\}$, $n(A \cap B) = 1$ and $n(A) + n(B) - n(A \cap B) = 4$.

Page 74

2-7 (a)   It is always true that: $A \cap (B \cap C) = (A \cap B) \cap C$.

The following figure gives Venn diagrams of each side of the above equation. Because the Venn diagrams result in the same set, the equation is always true.

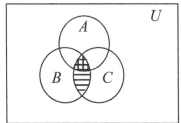 $B \cap C \equiv$
$A \cap (B \cap C) \boxplus$

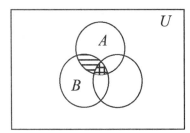 $A \cap B \equiv$
$(A \cap B) \cap C \boxplus$

(b)   It is always true that: $A \cup (B \cup C) = (A \cup B) \cup C$.

The following Venn diagrams justify this statement.

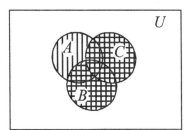 $B \cup C \equiv$
$A \cup (B \cup C) \,||||$

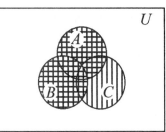 $A \cup B \equiv$
$(A \cup B) \cup C \,||||$

(c)   In general: $A - (B - C) \neq (A - B) - C$.

To see this, consider the following counterexample.

$$A = \{1, 2, 3, 4, 5\}$$
$$B = \{1, 2, 3\}$$
$$C = \{3, 4\}$$

Then $A - (B - C) = A - \{1, 2\} = \{3, 4, 5\}$.
But $(A - B) - C = \{4, 5\} - C = \{5\}$.

Thus for the above choice of A, B and C, we have that $A - (B - C) \neq (A - B) - C$

Page 76

2-8   The following Venn diagrams show $A \cup (B \cap C) = (A \cup B) \cap (A \cup C)$.

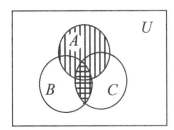 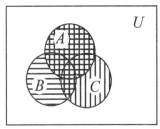 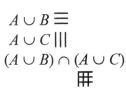

Page 84

2-9   For example, if the sets of elements are $\{a, b, c\}$ and $\{a, d\}$, then the union of the sets of elements is $\{a, b, c, d\}$. The union has only 4 elements while the original sets have 3 and 2 respectively. The sum of 3 and 2 is 5 not 4, the number of elements in the set union.

Page 94

2-10   One possible explanation is as follows: the first shirt can be worn with each of the 5 pairs of pants for a total of 5 different outfits. Also, the second shirt can be worn with each of the 5 pairs of pants for a total of 5 outfits different from the previous outfits. Similarly, the 3rd, 4th, 5th, and 6th shirts can be combined with the 5 pairs of pants for new outfits. In this way, each of the 6 shirts can be used for 5 new outfits for a total $5 + 5 + 5 + 5 + 5 + 5 = 6 \cdot 5$ outfits.

Page 107

2-11   Each is a function from the set of natural numbers to $\{0, 1\}$, because for each natural number there is a unique output in $\{0, 1\}$

Page 111

2-12   No. To see why, notice that C $(10.5) = 27 \cdot 10.5 = 283.5$ cents $\doteq 284$ cents $= \$2.84$. But, as explained in the text, the telephone company will charge $27 \cdot 11 = 297$ cents $= \$2.97$

The 13-cent discrepancy arises from the fact that a customer is charged for each whole minute and for an extra full minute, for any part of a minute that was started but not finished. Notice that the cost function $C = 27t$ is only valid for natural numbers t.

Page 126

3-1 a.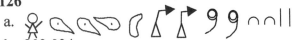

b. 203,034

c. Answers vary, for example, writing large numbers is very cumbersome as the system is additive rather than using place value. Performing operations involving addition, subtraction, multiplication, and division is also very hard because of way that numbers are represented.

Page 127

3-2 a.

b. $2 \cdot 60^2 + 11 \cdot 60 + 1 = 7861$.

c. The Hindu Arabic system has a symbol for 0 and this is very important in a system that uses place value. Because it uses base sixty, the Babylonian system requires the use of many symbols to write numbers such as 59.

Page 131

3-3 The illustration indicates successive divisions by 5's. This shows that there are 164 five's in 824 with 4 as a remainder. Next there are 32 five's in 164 with 4 five's as a remainder. Equivalently we could say that there are 25 five's in 824 with 4 five's and 4 units as a remainder. This process continues until we see that there is 1 625 in 824 with 1 125; 2 25's; 4 5's; and 4 units in 824.

Page 141

3-4 To use a number line for addition in base 5, a student will need to mark the line using base five numbers. For example, the line will need to be marked as shown below.

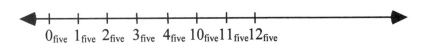

With such a number line as pictured, the addition is similar to addition in base ten on a number line.

Page 142

3-5 a.

+	0_{two}	1_{two}
0_{two}	1_{two}	1_{two}
1_{two}	1_{two}	10_{two}

b.
$$1101_{two}$$
$$-111_{two}$$
$$110_{two}$$

Page 147

3-6 The only time $a^n + a^m = a^{m+n}$ is when $a = 0$ and m and n are not zero.

Page 150
3-7   a. 40
      b. 6
      c. 6
      d. 0

Page159
3-8   Answers vary, for example,
      a. 40 + 160 = 200 and 29 + 31 = 60 so the sum is 260.
      b. 3679 – 400 = 3279 and 3279 – 74 = 3205.
      c. 75 + 25 = 100 and 100 + 3 = 103.
      d. 2500 – 500 = 200 and 2000 – 200 = 1800.

Page 160
3-9   Answers vary, for example,
      a.   4 • 25 = 100 and 32 • 100 = 3200.
      b. 123 • 3 = 100 • 3 + 23 • 3 = 300 + 69 = 369.
      c. 25 • 35 = (30 – 5)(30 + 5) = 30^2 – 25 = 900 – 25 = 875.
      d. 5075/25 = 5000/25 + 75/25 = 200 + 3 = 203.

Page 163
3-10 Answers vary, for example,
      a. To estimate 4525 • 9 we know 4525 • 10 = 45,250 and since we have only 9 sets of 4525 we can take away approximately 5000 from our estimate and we have 40,250.
      b. To estimate 3625/42 we know the answer will be close to 3600/40 or 90.

Page 178

4-1 (a)   Yes. Because $a - b = a + {}^-b$ and the sum of two integers is an integer.

(b)   None of the properties holds for integers because:
$a - b \neq b - a$ (if $a \neq b$)
$(a - b) - c \neq a - (b - c)$ (if $c \neq 0$)

There is no single integer i such that for all integers a $a - i = a$ and $i - a = a$ (the first equation implies that $i = 0$ but i does not satisfy the second equation).

Page 188

4-2 (a) $22 \cdot 18 = (20 + 2)(20 - 2) = 20^2 - 2^2 = 400 - 4 = 396$

(b) $24 \cdot 36 = (30 - 6)(30 + 6) = 30^2 - 6^2 = 900 - 36 = 864$

(c) $998 \cdot 1002 = (1000 - 2)(1000 + 2) = 1000^2 - 2^2 = 1,000,000 - 4 = 999,996$

Page 197

4-3   Yes, it is true. If $3 \mid x$, then 3 divides any numbers times x and in particular $3 \mid xy$.

Page 202

4-4 $1 + 2 + 5 + 0 + 6 + 5 = 19$, so we must find numbers x and y such that $9 \mid [19 + (x + y)]$. Any two numbers that sum to 8 or 17 will satisfy this. Therefore the blanks could be filled with 8 and 9, or 9 and 8, or 0 and 8, or 8 and 0.

Page 207

4-5 (a)   Answers vary. For example, only square numbers are listed in Column 3; 2 is the only even number that will ever be in Column 2; and Column 2 contains prime numbers. The powers of 2 appear in successive columns.

(b)   There will never be other entries in Column 1 because 1 is the only number with one factor. Other numbers have at least the number itself and 1.

(c)   49, 121, 169

(d)   64

(e)   The square numbers have an odd number of factors. Factors occur in pairs; for example, for 16 we have 1 and 16, 2 and 8, and 4 and 4. When we list the factors, we list only the distinct factors, so 4 is not listed twice, thereby making the number of factors of 16 an odd number. Similar reasoning holds for all square numbers.

Page 211

4-6 (a)   1, 2, 3, 6, 9

(b)   1, 2, 3, 4, 6, 8

(c)   Only white rods can be used to form one-color trains for prime numbers if two or more rods must be used.

(d)   8. The number must have at least factors of 1, 2, 3, 5, 6, 10, 15, and 30.

Page 212

4-7 (a) No, because the multiples of 2 have 2 as a factor.

(b) The multiples of 3 (3, 6, 9, 12, 15, . . .)

(c) The multiples of 5 (5, 10, 15, 20, . . .)

(d) The multiples of 7 (7, 14, 21, . . .)

(e) We have to check only divisibility by 2, 3, 5, and 7.

Page 221

4-8 The 1, 2, 3, and 6 rods can all be used to build both the 24 and 30 train. The greatest of these is 6, so $GCD\,(24, 30) = 6$.

Page 227

4-9 We use the 8 rod and the 10 rod and start building trains. We stop the first time the trains are the same lengths. This happens when we use five of the 8 rods and four of the 10 rods. Therefore the LCM is the length of the train, which is 40.

Page 235

4-10 (a) Yes

(b) Yes

(c) Yes, 0 is the identity

(d) Yes

Page 248

5-1 A Venn diagram depicting the relationship among natural numbers, whole numbers, integers and rational numbers follows:

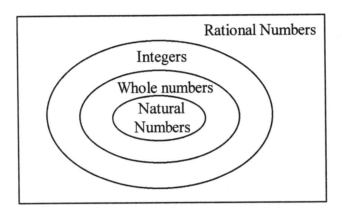

Page 252

5-2 Theorem 5-1 states that if a, b, and c are integers and $b > 0$, then $a/b > c/b$ if and only if $a > c$. The question is to investigate if the theorem is true if $b < 0$. Consider $2 > 1$ and $-1 < 0$. Now $2/(-1) < 1/(-1)$ which contradicts an expanded theorem when $b < 0$.

Page 253

5-3 $0 < \dfrac{a}{b} < \dfrac{c}{d}$ so that $0 < \dfrac{1}{2} \cdot \dfrac{a}{b} < \dfrac{1}{2} \cdot \dfrac{c}{d}$.

Also, $0 < \dfrac{a}{b} = \dfrac{1}{2} \cdot \dfrac{a}{b} + \dfrac{1}{2} \cdot \dfrac{a}{b} < \dfrac{1}{2} \cdot \dfrac{c}{d} = \dfrac{1}{2}\left(\dfrac{a}{b} + \dfrac{c}{d}\right)$.

Similarly, $0 < \dfrac{1}{2}\left(\dfrac{a}{b} + \dfrac{c}{d}\right) < \dfrac{c}{d}$,

and therefore, $0 < \dfrac{a}{b} < \dfrac{1}{2}\left(\dfrac{a}{b} + \dfrac{c}{d}\right) < \dfrac{c}{d}$.

Page 297

6-1   The cartoon reports the cost of prime rib is .75¢ which is not one half of $1.50. If the waiter intended the price of the prime rib to be one half the price of the steak, then the amount should be written as $.75 or 75¢. The notation .75¢ indicates .75 of one cent. This mistake is commonly made in stores when the money amount is less than one dollar, for example, an item is marked for .50¢ when it really should be $.50 or 50¢.

Page 305

6-2 $3.6 \cdot 1000 = 3.6 \cdot 10^3 = (3 + \dfrac{6}{10}) \cdot 10^3 = 3 \cdot 10^3 + \dfrac{6}{10} \cdot 10^3 = 3 \cdot 10^3 + 6 \cdot 10^2 =$
$3 \cdot 10^3 + 6 \cdot 10^2 + 0 \cdot 10^1 + 0 \cdot 1 = 3600$. Thus, we see that multiplication by 1000 results in moving the decimal point three places to the right. In general, multiplication by 10^n, where n is a positive integer, results in moving the decimal point n places to the right.

Page 308

6-3 $1.19/32 oz is about $0.037/oz while $1.43/48 oz is abut $0.030/oz so the 48 oz jar is a better buy.

Page 311

6-4   Answers vary, for example, using the front digits the first estimate is $2 + 0 + 6 + 4 + 5 =$ $17. Next, we adjust the estimate. Because $0.89 + $0.13 is about $1.00 and $0.75 + $.05 is $0.80 and $0.80 + $0.39 is about $1.20, the adjustment is $2.20 and the estimate is $19.20.

Page 315

6-5   (a) $1/9 = 0.\overline{1}$

(b)   i. $2/9 = 2(0.\overline{1}) = 0.\overline{2}$ ii. $3/9 = 3(0.\overline{1}) = 0.\overline{3}$
         iii. $5/9 = 5(0.\overline{1}) = 0.\overline{4}$ iv. $8/9 = 8(0.\overline{1}) = 0.\overline{8}$

Page 318

6-6   (a)   Approximately 42.47753... . The decimal is nonterminating because $(207/365) \cdot 749/10 = (207 \cdot 749) / 3650 = (3 \cdot 3 \cdot 23 \cdot 7 \cdot 107) / 2 \cdot 5 \cdot 5 \cdot 73$ and the fraction in simplest form has factors other than 2s and 5s in the denominator.

(b)   Arlo's age in years and months is 42 years and approximately 5.7 months.

Page 322

6-7   (a)   Answers vary, for example, most calculators will convert the decimal form of a number to a percent by moving the decimal point two places to the left. Others calculators actually place a % symbol in the display when the $\boxed{\%}$ key is pushed.

(b) $33.\overline{3}\%$

Page 343

6-8 (a) The approach works because $\sqrt{\sqrt{\sqrt{a}}} = \left(\left(a^{\frac{1}{2}}\right)^{\frac{1}{2}}\right)^{\frac{1}{2}} = \left(a^{\frac{1}{4}}\right)^{\frac{1}{2}}$

$$= a^{\frac{1}{8}}$$

$$= \sqrt[8]{a}$$

(b) For $n = 2^k$, where k is a positive integer. As shown in part (a), repeatedly applying the square root function to a we get $a^{\overbrace{\frac{1}{2}\frac{1}{2}\frac{1}{2}\cdots\frac{1}{2}}^{k \text{ times}}}$ or $a^{\frac{1}{2^k}} = \sqrt[2^k]{a}$.

Page 352

7-1 (a)   1

   (b)   1

   (c)   Yes, they always sum to 1 that is the sum of the probabilities of all the different elements in the sample space.

Page 367

7-2 (a) $\dfrac{6}{15} + \dfrac{4}{15} = \dfrac{10}{15}$ or $\dfrac{4}{9}$

   (b) $\dfrac{4}{15} + \dfrac{1}{15} = \dfrac{5}{15}$ or $\dfrac{1}{3}$

   (c) $\dfrac{4}{15} + \dfrac{4}{15} = \dfrac{8}{15}$

Page 368

7-3 (a)   Yes

   (b)   With replacement: any game with the same number of white and colored marbles. Without replacement: 3 colored and 6 white or 3 white and 6 colored, 6 colored and 10 white or 6 white and 10 colored marbles.

   (c)   Without replacement the white and colored marbles need to be two consecutive triangular numbers, that is $1+2+3+...n$ and $1+2+3+...n+n+1$ (this is easier to discover and verify using combinations introduced in Section 7-5).

Page 379

7-4 (a)   Answers vary.

   (b) $\dfrac{3}{8}$

   (d)   No, simulations will not always result in the same probability as the theoretical probability. However, if the experiment is repeated a great number of times, the simulated probability should approach the theoretical probability.

Page 387

7-5 (b)   There is one way to toss a head and one way of not tossing a head, so the odds in favor are 1:1.

   (c)   There are four ways to draw an ace and 48 ways of not drawing an ace, so the odds in favor are 4:48 or 1:12.

   (e)   There are 13 ways of drawing a heart and 39 ways of not drawing a heart, so the odds in favor are 13:39 or 1:3.

Page 393

7-6 (a) $n(n-1), n(n-1)(n-2), n(n-1)(n-1)(n-3)$.

   (b) $n(n-1), n(n-1)(n-2)...(n-r+1)$

Page 394

7-7 (a)   We get an error message because 100! and 98! are too large for the calculator to handle.

   (b) $\dfrac{100!}{98!} = \dfrac{98!\cdot 99\cdot 100}{98!} = 9900$

Page 410

8-1   The person is filling the bathtub as we see the water level increasing over time. The water is then shut off and the water level is constant. Next the person enters the tub and the water level increases instantly. The person takes a bath and then gets out of the tub and then lets the water drain out of the tub.

Page 415

8-2   It appears that the fifth-period class did better. We can see that there are more scores grouped toward the bottom, which is where the higher grades are located. We can easily determine that the median for the second-period class is 78.5 and the median for the fifth-period class is 85 and this again shows that the fifth period class did better.

Page 421

8-3   (a)   A histogram is more appropriate to compare numbers of data that are grouped into numerical intervals. With the line graph there appears to be a frequency for *Times per month* such as 4.5 etc.

(b)   A circle graph is appropriate for showing the division of a whole into parts.

(c)   A line graph is appropriate for showing how data values change over time.

Page 430

8-4   (a) Answers vary, for example, all the puppies could weigh 7 lb. Then $(7 \cdot 7)/7 = 7$ lb. Another possibility is 4, 5, 6, 7, 8, 9, 10. The mean for these scores is also 7.

(b)   If all the scores were equal, then the mean is equal to the high score and also the low score.

Page 432

8-5   (a)   The average of 2.58 could only be a mean. To be a mode it would have to be a whole number. To be a median it would have to be a whole number or end in .5.

(b)   The average of 2.5 could be a mean or a median. It could not be a mode since the mode for the number of children must be a whole number.

Page 440

8-6   One probably would not expect any outliers because the lower end of the salary scale was dropped. One would expect all the five-number summary points to increase. There will probably little noticeable difference in the story the data tells.

Page 465

9-1 (a) Exactly one line can be drawn through any two points.

(b) Skew lines cannot be parallel. By definition, parallel lines are in the same planes. Skew lines are not.

(c) Let O be the center of the globe. First consider two points A and B on the globe which are the endpoints of a diameter, that is, A, O, and B are collinear. There are infinitely many planes containing A and B and hence the center of the globe, O. Each of these planes intersects the globe in a "great" circle. Consequently if A, O, B are collinear, there is no unique "line" through A and B.

Page 477

9-2 An example follows. The figure crosses itself and is not simple. Also it is not closed.

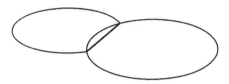

Page 477

9-3 One approach to this problem is to start shading the area surrounding point X. If we stay between the lines, we should be able to decide whether the shaded area is inside our outside the curve.

The shaded part of the figure below indicates that point X is located outside the curve.

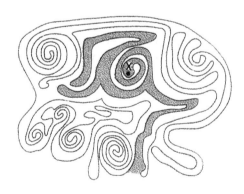

Page 482

9-4 (1) True. From the definition (Table 9-6) we know that an equilateral triangle has three congruent angles. Therefore it has at least two congruent sides and hence it is isosceles.

(2) True. By definition, a regular quadrilateral is a four-sided figure that is both, equilateral and equiangular. A square has four sides of equal length and four right angles—so a square is a regular quadrilateral.

(3) True. Because a rhombus is a parallelogram and a rectangle is a parallelogram with a right angle, if one angle of a rhombus is a right angle then all of its angles are right.

(4) True; follows from part (3).

Page 482

9-4   (5)   True, because a rectangle is a parallelogram and if one angle of a parallelogram is a right angle all its angles are right angles.

   (6)   True. A rectangle is a trapezoid since it is a quadrilateral with at least one pair of parallel sides.

   (7)   True. A square is a rectangle that is an isosceles trapezoid. Also a square is a kite. Hence there are isosceles trapezoids which are kites.

   (8)   False as shown in the figure below.

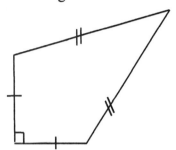

Page 488

9-5   (a)   The amount of turning that takes place when one "walks around the triangle and ends up pointed in the same direction in which you started" is 360°. Thus the sum of the measure of the exterior angles of the triangle is 360°.

   (b)   With both the exterior and interior angles of a triangle, there are three sets of supplementary angles having a total sum of 540° for their measures. Subtracting the sum of the measures of the exterior angles from the total sum, we have 540° - 360°, or 180° for the sum of the measure of the interior angles of the triangle.

   (c)   The sum of the measures of the exterior angles for any convex polygon is 360° for the same reason as given in part a.

Page 490

9-6   (a)   There are infinitely many. Consider the number of lines of longitude on the globe.

   (b)   A spherical triangle could have as vertices the North Pole, Quito, Ecuador, and Kisumu, Kenya.

   (c)   Consider any triangle with the North Pole as one vertex and the other two vertices on the equator such that the angle formed at the North Pole is a right angle.

   (d)   The sum of the measures has to be less than or equal to 540°.

Page 491

9-7   Any convex polygon of n sides can be separated into $n - 2$ triangles by drawing all the diagonals from one vertex of the polygon. The sum of the measures of these triangles is $180(n - 2)$. The result is the same as that of Theorem 9-4.

Page 501

9-8   (a) $V + F - E = 2$

   (b)   The relationship is true for any polyhedron.

Page 508

9-9   (a)   There can be no traversable network with more than two odd vertices. An odd vertex must be either a starting point of a stopping point of the path.

   (b)   This is not possible.

Page 522

10-1 There are six possible ways to write the congruence: ABC paired with $A'B'C'$, ACB paired with $A'C'B'$, BAC paired with $B'A'C'$, BCA paired with $B'C'A'$, CAB paired with $C'A'B'$, and CBA paired with $C'B'A'$.

Page 525

10-2 (a) In order to construct a triangle from three lengths of straws, the length of one piece must be greater than the lengths of the other two pieces.

(b) The triangle would be equilateral and equiangular.

(c) There can be no triangle constructed. The three pieces would lie along a segment.

(d) Yes. See the answer to part a.

Page 529

10-3 Draw two intersecting arcs with the same radius, one with center at A and the other with center at B. The two points of intersection are opposite vertices of a rhombus. The line connecting the points is the perpendicular bisector of the segment.

Page 530

10-4 (a) The triangles do not have to be congruent. An example is seen in the following drawing.

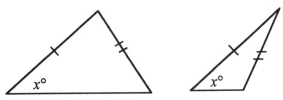

(b) If the non-included angle is a right angle, the triangles are congruent. More generally, if the non-included angle is opposite the larger of the two sides, the triangles are congruent.

Page 535

10-5 In a parallelogram $ABCD$ opposite sides are parallel. This implies that $\angle BAC \cong \angle ACD$ as well as $\angle BCA \cong \angle DAC$. Hence, $\triangle ABC \cong \triangle CDA$ by ASA since $\overline{AC}$ is a common side. By $CPCT$, $\overline{AB} \cong \overline{CD}$ and $\overline{BC} \cong \overline{DA}$.

Page 536

10-6 Yes. If $ABCD$ is a quadrilateral whose diagonals intersect at M, then congruent vertical angles with vertex at M are formed. Because the diagonals bisect each other, it follows from SAS that $\triangle AMD \cong \triangle CMB$. Hence, $\angle MAD \cong \angle MCB$ and therefore $\overline{BC}$ is parallel to $\overline{AD}$. In a similar way we can show that $\overline{AB}$ is parallel to $\overline{DC}$ and hence $ABCD$ is a parallelogram.

Page 541

10-7 One way to accomplish the construction is to place the hypotenuse of the triangle on the given line and to place the ruler so that one of the legs of the triangle will be on the ruler. Now, keeping the ruler fixed, slide the triangle so that the side of the triangle on the ruler touches the ruler all the time. Slide the triangle on the ruler until the given point is on the hypotenuse. The line containing the hypotenuse is parallel to the given line.

Page 546

10-8 One way is to consider the equivalent contrapositive statement: If a point is not on the angle bisector of an angle then it is not equidistant from the sides of the angle. Choose points not on the angle bisector of an angle and use the measurement tool to see that for each point the distances to the sides of the angle are not the same. It is possible to prove the original statement by using the Hypotenuse-Leg Congruency Theorem (if the hypotenuse and one leg of one right triangle are correspondingly congruent to the hypotenuse and a leg of another right triangle, then the triangles are congruent).

Page 554

10-9 The statement is not true for polygons. For example a rectangle and a square have congruent angles but do not have to be similar.

Page 556

10-10 The triangles formed are similar and one would expect the segments cut by the parallel segments to have proportional lengths. They do not. Thus, there is the possibility for a misleading graph.

Page 570

10-11 If we graph the equation $y = mx$ for small values of m like $m = 0.1$ and $m = 0.01$ we see that when m gets close to 0, the line gets closer to the x-axis.

Page 575

10-12 (a) All the points on a horizontal line have the same y–coordinate. Thus, two points on a horizontal line have the form (x_1, y_1) and (x^2, y^2) where $y_2 = y_1$. The slope is

$$\frac{y_2 - y_1}{x_2 - x_1} = \frac{0}{x_2 - x_1} = 0.$$

(b) For any vertical line $x_2 = x_1$ and therefore $x_2 - x_1 = 0$. If we attempted to find the slope we would have to divide by 0, which is impossible. Hence the slope of a vertical line is not defined.

Page 580

10-13 (a) The graphs are lines that intersect at $x = 4$ and $y = 3$.

(b) The lines are parallel and hence the system has no solution. Algebraic approach: assuming that there is a solution x and y, we multiply the first equation by 2 and add it side by side to the second. Therefore, x and y must satisfy: $0 \cdot x + 0 \cdot y = 7$.

However, no x and y satisfies the above equation (a solution would imply $0 = 7$). This contradicts our assumption that the original system has a solution.

(c) The graphs are lines that intersect at $x = \dfrac{1}{5}$ and $y = \dfrac{^-1}{5}$.

Page 597
11-1 (a) 115   (b) 55

Page 605
11-2 (a) 12   (b) 6   (c) 4

Page 609
11-3 Approximately 259 cm^2

Page 609
11-4 (a) The areas of the parallelogram and the rectangle are the same because they are composed of the same two pieces and the area of the figures is the sum of the areas of the two pieces.

   (b) The formula for the area of a rectangle is $A = \ell w$. The length of the new rectangle is just base b of the parallelogram and the width of the rectangle is just the height of the parallelogram. Therefore, the formula for the area of the parallelogram is $A = bh$.

Page 611
11-5 The new figure is a parallelogram with base $(b_1 + b_2)$ and height h, where b_1 and b_2 are the bases of the original trapezoid. The area of the parallelogram is $A = h(b_1 + b_2)$. Because this is twice the area of the original trapezoid, we divide by 2 to obtain $A = h/2(b_1 + b_2)$ which is the formula for the area of the original trapezoid.

Page 624
11-6 The square on one leg that is labeled 1 could be cut off and placed in the dashed space on the square of the hypotenuse. Then pieces 2, 3, 4, and 5 could be cut off and placed around piece 1 so that the square on the hypotenuse is filled exactly with the 5 pieces. This shows that the sum of the areas of the squares on the two legs of a right triangle is equal to the area on the square of the hypotenuse.

Page 628
11-7 (a) You could build the triangle and then measure the angles to see if there was a right angle. If the angle is a right angle, then the triangle is a right triangle. You could measure the three sides and use the converse of the Pythagorean Theorem to see if a right triangle is formed.

   (b) If the three lengths of a right triangle are multiplied by a fixed number, then the resulting lengths determine a right triangle, for example, if the right triangle lengths are 3-4-5, and the fixed number is 5, then 15-20-25 is a right triangle.

   (c) If the three lengths of a right triangle are multiplied by a fixed number, then the resulting numbers determine a right triangle.

Page 630
11-8 It makes no difference in the Distance Formula if $(x_1 - x_2)$ and $(y_1 - y_2)$ are used instead of $(x_1 - x_2)$ and $(y_1 - y_2)$ respectively. Because both quantities in the formula are squared, the result is the same whether the difference is positive or negative.

Page 636

11-9   (a) $S.A. = 2 \cdot (5/2) \cdot 8 + 2 \cdot (8 \cdot 11) + 2 \cdot (5/2) \cdot 11 = 271$ in.^{2}.

(b)   No, the rectangle would have to be 21 in. by 16 in. .

Page 637

11-10   Because we want the surface area of a right prism, we must include the top and bottom so we need $2B$ (where B is the area of the base which is the same as the area of the top) in the formula $S.A. = ph + 2B$. From the net, we see that the lateral surface area opens up into a rectangle that has width equal to the height, h. The length of the rectangle is equal to the sum of the lengths of the sides of the base which is the perimeter of the base.

Therefore the area of the rectangle (lateral surface area of the prism) is $A = \ell w = ph$. Hence the surface area for any right prism is given by $S.A. = ph + 2B$.

Page 645

11-11   (a)   Both figures have a volume of 9 cubic units.

(b)   No, the second figure has the greater surface area.

(c)   The first figure has surface area 34 square units and the second figure has area 36 square units.

Page 650

11-12   (a)   The two figures have bases in the same plane and the figures have the same height. Figure 11-73 shows that if a plane parallel to the base is passed through the figures, then equal areas are obtained. By Cavalieri's Principle these two figures have equal volumes.

(b)   (i)   By Cavalieri's Principle the volumes are the same.

(ii)   By Cavalieri's Principle the volumes are the same.

Page 656

11-13   (a) 1 g   (b) 1 kg   (c) 1 dm^3 (d) 1 mL

(e) 1 g   (f) 1 kL   (g) 1 t

Page 658

11-14   Yes, when it is ⁻40 degrees Celsius it is ⁻40 degrees Fahrenheit.

Page 671

12-1   a.   One way to do this is to connect A and M. Draw a line parallel to line MN through A; find a point A' so that $MN = AA'$.

b.   The direction of $\overrightarrow{AA'}$ must be the same as that of the direction of $\overrightarrow{MN}$.

Page 675

12-2   Draw a circle with center O and radius OP. Next draw the same size circle with center the angle given. Use your compass to measure the are of the circle cut off by the angle. On circle O, mark the image P' of P.

Page 680

12-3   Hint: Construct a perpendicular from P to line m. Find P' so that line m is the perpendicular bisector of $\overline{PP'}$. Points P and P' are the endpoints of a diagonal of a rhombus. The other diagonal lies along line m.

Page 689

12-4   Find the line so that the figure folds onto the image. The fold line is the reflecting line.

Page 717

12-5   Continue to create the shapes and rotate them to form the tessellation.

Appendix I

Page 738

AI-1   TO CIRCLE1
        REPEAT 360 [FD 1 RT 1]
    END

Appendix II

Page 749

AII-1   a.   The values displayed using $\boxed{\text{TRACE}}$ are the exact values in L1 and L2.

b.   Only points are displayed because this is the graph of the ordered pairs where the x-value comes from L1 and the y-value is the corresponding value from L2.

c.   A linear pattern is shown on the graph; that is, all the points fall along a line.

d.   Depending on the window, the cost of 12 CD's can be obtained from the graph of

$y = 12.95x + 5$ by using the $\boxed{\text{TRACE}}$ feature.

Chapter 1
Page 35   The number of moves is $2^n - 1$ for n disks. For three coins, the number of moves is 7. For four coins, the number of moves is 15.

At the rate of one move per second, it would take approximately 58,455,805,0418 years to move 64 disks.

Chapter 2
Page 82   1. All green blocks or all large blocks. All large blocks or all green blocks. The sets are equal.
2. All blocks which are not in the set of all green blocks or all large blocks. All the small blocks which are red, yellow, or blue. The sets are equal.
3. Blocks which are not both green and large. All non-green or all small blocks. The sets are equal.
4. All the green blocks which are not large. All the small green blocks. The sets are equal.

Page 102   The problem assumes that a positive whole number is entered.
1. Yes.
2. 18 and 19.
3. In general, even numbers appear to reach 1 quicker.
4. Answers depend on choices.

Chapter 3
Page 145   Either abacus may be used. Both are comparable. Some may prefer the suan pan because there are two counters above the bar and five below the bar.

Page 156   1. (a) A computer
2. (a) When a person tells his or her age by listing cards, the person is giving the base-two representation for his or her age. The number can then be determined by adding the numbers in the upper left-hand corners of the named cards.
    (b) Card F would have 32 in the upper left corner. Each of the numbers 1 through 63 could be written in base two so you can tell where to place them on the cards.

Chapter 4
Page 219   Yes, each of the primes on the diagonal can be obtained from the formula. The reason is as follows:

Because of the geometrical structure of the spiral, the "distance" from the center square (where 41 is located) to the next square on the diagonal along the spiral is 2 steps. From there to the next one on the diagonal along the spiral, 4 steps, and from there to the next, 6 steps, and so on. In general, from any spot on the diagonal to the next one on the diagonal along the spiral is 2 steps further than it took to reach the

Chapter 4 (cont.)

previous spot on the diagonal. It can be checked (there is no other known way) that for $0 \le n \le 39$ the formula $n^2 + n + 41$ yields primes. For $n = 0$ we get 41. Whenever $n^2 + n + 41$ is known, the next number resulting from the formula is $(n + 1)^2 + (n + 1) + 41 = (n^2 + n + 41) + 2(n + 1)$. Thus, for $0 \le n \le 38$ whenever $n^2 + n + 41$ yields a prime the next prime obtained from the formula is $2n + 2$ steps away and hence, as explained earlier, on the diagonal. Notice that the spiral can be continued with only primes in the diagonal up to $n = 39$, that is until we get $30^2 + 39 + 41$ or 1601. For $n = 40$ we get $1601 + 2(39 + 1)$ or $1681 = 41^2$, which will end up on the diagonal (because it is $2 \cdot 40$ steps away from 1601) but not a prime.

Chapter 5 There are none in this chapter.

Chapter 6 There are none in this chapter.

Chapter 7
Page 361 Answers vary
Page 362 Answers vary

Chapter 8
Page 447
1. (a) 60   (b) 57, 58   (c) 57, 58, 59, 61
2. The mean in each case is 56 and that is also the number in the middle of the strip.
3. The mean would not change as the balance point does not change.
4. The median is 56 and the mode is 98
5. There is not a balance around the median or mode.
6. If the median or mode is equal to the mean then there would be balance.

Chapter 9
Page 475
(a) By folding a crease onto itself, we have created two angles that are both supplementary and congruent. They must have measure 90° making the creases perpendicular.
(b) One obtains a 45° angle by bisecting the 90° angle.
The 135° angle is 90° + 45°.
The 22°30' angle is obtained by bisecting the 45° angle.

Page 506 One needs to use cubes to build the structure. Is there more than one that meets the specifications?

Page 512
(a) It has only one side.
(b) Cutting once produces a single long strip that is two-sided.
(c) The result is two strips intertwined. One is a Möibus strip while the other is a two-sided hoop.
(d) There are three loops now though you cannot do this with a continuous cut.

Chapter 10

Page 560 The pantograph is designed so that point E must be fixed (nailed to a table or a board), the strips pivoted A, B, C, and D and $ABCD$ is a parallelogram. Also, points E, D, and F are colinear (it can be shown that E, D, and F are colinear for a particular position of the pantograph, then the three points will be colinear for every position of the pantograph). Because $\overline{CD}$ is parallel to $\overline{BF}$ we have: $\dfrac{EF}{CD} = \dfrac{BE}{EC}$. Since $\dfrac{BE}{EC}$ is fixed (the same for every position of the pantograph) it follows that $\dfrac{EF}{CD}$ is fixed; it equals some real number r. This implies that if D' and F' are new positions of the pointer and the pencil, then $\dfrac{EF'}{ED'} = \dfrac{EF}{ED} = r$. If the pointer traces the segment DD', the pencil will draw the segment FF' and $\dfrac{FF'}{DD'} = r$. Because each segment traced is enlarged by the same factor r, when any figure is traced, the pencil will draw a similar figure. This can be explained in a simpler way using the concept of a size transformation in Chapter 12 (the size transformation has center E and scale factor r).

Chapter 11

Page 600   Answers vary but the average should be approximately 3.1.

Chapter 12

Page 703   It is always possible to find such a line. The line, x, needed is such that the angle formed by lines m and n in that order is the same as the angle formed by the lines x and p in that order.

Page 718   Answers will depend upon the type of patterns chosen. Each group should tessellate the plane.

Chapter 1
Page 18 Possible answers are the following:

Column D: To find the value in cell Dn, add the values in cells An and Bn.

Column E: To find the value in cell En, subtract the value in cell An from the value in cell Bn.

Column F: To find the value in cell Fn, multiply the value in cell An times the value in cell Bn.

Column G: To find the value in cell Gn, multiply the value in cell An by 2 and add 6.

Column H: To find the value in cell Hn, multiply the value in cell An times 2 and add the value in cell Bn.

Column I: To find the value in cell In, add 1 to the value in cell Fn.

Chapter 2
Page 114 All graphs are straight lines parallel to the straight line $y = 2x + 1$. Reason: The graphs of $y = 2x + b$ are straight lines for different choices of b. The lines are parallel because the system of equations $y = 2x + 1$ and $y = 2x + b$ where $b \neq 1$ have no solution, which implies that the lines do not intersect.

Chapter 3 There are none in this chapter.

Chapter 4
Page 173 The entries in column A stay 4 while the entries in column B start with 3 and decrease by 1. The sum of columns A and B is entered in column C starting with 7. The entries in column C are the integers in decreasing order starting with 7. The patterns show that the sum of two positive numbers is positive. The sum of a positive and a negative number is positive if the absolute value of the positive number is greater than the absolute value of the negative number. The sum of 0 if both numbers have the same absolute value. The sum is negative otherwise.

Similar results can be obtained if column A is changed to $^-4$.

Page 180 (a) The graph should appear as shown below.

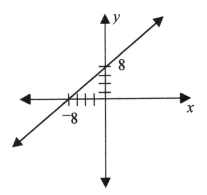

(b) When x is less than $^-4$, the y-values are negative; when $x = ^-4$, $y = 0$; when x is greater than $^-4$, the y-values are positive.

Chapter 4 (cont.)
Page 183 If the Logo program is run, the following outputs are obtained.
   (a) 7   (b) 0   (c) 140   (d) 21

Page 184 The product of two negative numbers is a positive number. The numbers in the C column are perfect squares.

Page 206 (a) This program will print "OKAY" if :N is divisible by :X and print "NOT DIVISIBLE" otherwise.
       (b) The integer division button gives more information. If the first number is not divisible by the second number, it will show a remainder of 0.

Page 220 Same answer as for problem 3 in Ongoing Assessment 4-4.

Page 220 (a) prime
       (b) not prime
       (c) not prime
       (d) prime
       (e) prime
       (f) not prime

Page 233 1. The intersection is the first twelve multiples of 12.
       2. You only need to fill down to 47.
       3. (a) 180
          (b) You need to use one of the techniques in the section to find LCM (6, 9, 12, 15).
       4. (a) GCD(676, 221) = 13
          (b) GCD(10,764, 2300) = 92
       5. TO LCM :A :B
          OUTPUT (:A * :B)/GCD :A :B
          END

Chapter 5
Page 256 2/7

Chapter 6
Page 319 $\dfrac{1}{11} = 0.\overline{09}$

$\dfrac{1}{17} = 0.\overline{0588235294117647}$

$\dfrac{1}{29} = 0.\overline{0344827586206896551724137931}$

Page 331 Answers vary.

Chapter 7
Page 362 Answers vary.
Page 378 Answers vary.

Chapter 8
Page 447 The mean is 46. The standard deviation is approximately 8.85. The variance is approximately 78.32.

Chapter 9
Page 475 (a)   A segment will be drawn down that is 50 turtle steps long.
(b)   A segment will be drawn down that is 50 turtle steps long.
(c)   A square of size 50 will be drawn.
(d)   A pentagon with sides of size 60 will be drawn.
(e)   A five-pointed star with sides of size 60 will be drawn.

Page 484 (a) A sequence of commands could be the following:
```
TO SPINSQ :SIDE
    REPEAT 6 [SQUARE :SIDE RIGHT 60]
END
TO SQUARE :SIDE
    REPEAT 4 [FORWARD :SIDE RIGHT 90]
END
```
(b) A sequence of commands could be the following:
```
TO SPINSQ :SIDE
    REPEAT 10 [SQUARE :SIDE RIGHT 36]
END
TO SQUARE :SIDE
    REPEAT 4 [FORWARD :SIDE RIGHT 90]
END
```

Page 506
The method of drawing depends totally on the type of technology being used.

Chapter 10
Page 533 1. Answers may vary. For example.
```
TO EOUITRI :SIDE
    REPEAT 3 [FD :SIDE RT 120]
END
```
2. (a)   A triangle is constructed because the computer does not know the difference between an angle measure and a compass heading.
(b)   No. A triangle cannot have an angle with measure 190°.
(c)   Add the following:
IF NOT (:ANGLE <180) PRINT [NO TRIANGLE IS POSSIBLE.] STOP

Page 550 1. (c) m($\angle BOC$) = 2m ($\angle BPC$)
2. The angle is a right angle.

Chapter 10 (cont.)
Page 564-566

The perimeter of the S_1 is 3; the perimeter of S_2 is 4; and the perimeter of S_3 is 48/9. Students may have trouble thinking about the perimeters of the snowflake curves.

Chapter 11
Page 599   Answers vary, for example, to draw a smaller circle we might use

```
TO CIRCLE2
      REPEAT 180[FD 1 RT 2]
END
```
To draw a larger circle we might use
```
TO CIRCLE3
REPEAT 360[FD 2 RT 1]
END
```

Page 635   (a)   Answers vary depending on the lengths of the sides.

(b)   Answers vary depending on the lengths of the sides

(c)   The length of the hypotenuse of a 45-45-90 degree triangle is $\sqrt{2}$ times the length of a leg.

(d)   The length of the hypotenuse in a 30-60-90 degree triangle is 2 times the length of the leg opposite the 30-degree angle and the length of the leg opposite the 60-degree angle is $\sqrt{3}$ times the length of the short leg.

Page 644   The answers to all the parts will depend on the nets that are chosen.

Chapter 12
Page 683   An equilateral triangle has 120° rotational symmetry. Other triangles do not have this property.

Page 695   The resulting drawings may depend upon your Logo. However, we expect the following:

(a)

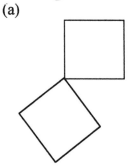

Chapter 12 (cont.)

(b)

(c)

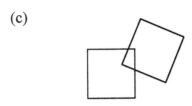

Page 712 Figures (a), (c) and (d) all have turn symmetries. Figure (b) has one turn symmetry through the middle black dot.